By HILDA WHITE

WILD DECEMBERS, A *Biographical Portrait of the Brontës*
SONG WITHOUT END, *The Love Story of Clara and Robert Schumann*

SONG WITHOUT END

The Love Story of Clara and Robert Schumann

SONG WITHOUT END

The Love Story of

Clara and Robert Schumann

by

HILDA WHITE

E. P. DUTTON & CO., INC.

NEW YORK, 1959

Poems appearing on pages 86 and 116
are reprinted from THE POETRY AND
PROSE OF HEINRICH HEINE, edited
by Frederic Ewen, translated by Aaron
Kramer, by permission of The Citadel
Press, New York.

Selection appearing on page 281 from
"On Schubert's C Major Symphony" by
Robert Schumann is reprinted from THE
COMPOSER AS LISTENER, edited by
Irving Kolodin, by permission of Horizon
Press, New York. Copyright 1958 by
Irving Kolodin.

LIBRARY OF CONGRESS CATALOG CARD NUMBER: 59-11503

For Arthur, my husband,
with deepest love and gratitude

CONTENTS

"Through all the tones in Earth's many-colored dream
There sounds for the secret listener
One soft, long-drawn note."

F<small>RIEDRICH</small> S<small>CHLEGEL</small>

Inscribed on Robert Schumann's Fantasia, Op. 17.
To Clara he wrote: "It is a deep lament for you."

AUTHOR'S NOTE

To HIS FRIEND, Töpken, Schumann once wrote: "We are living a romance such as has never, perhaps, been told in a book." He was not, of course, referring to himself and his beloved Clara, but to all the participants in music's great Romantic Movement of which he was such an outstanding leader. Subsequently, more than one scholar painstakingly recorded *that* "romance." It is not, then, the purpose of *Song Without End* to do more than fit our picture to the size of our frame. What we draw here, first and foremost, is a remarkable love story with Robert Schumann's whisper always in our ear, "Be true to us, my Clara and me."

As she appears in these pages, Clara is still a groping young girl finding her way through to maturity. But the time was to come when she would prove herself all that Schumann knew her to be, a woman of outstanding courage and strength, steadily gaining through the years in artistry and understanding. In her diary, a few days before her marriage, she reveals to us her fears that she could never achieve the intellectual heights befitting the wife of Robert Schumann. But she was apparently far too modest. It was of Clara Schumann that Johannes Brahms spoke when he said that he would not offer his compositions to the public until *she* had first given approval.

Love, hardship, and eventual tragedy molded Clara into a woman of noble stature. Her marriage did indeed bring her more than her share of the troubles of which her father had been so sorely afraid. But to her everlasting credit she did not once falter. She lived up to her vow to shelter her husband from "all the prosaic things of domestic life" so that he might give to the world his exquisite songs. And when her time of mourning came, when only too soon Schumann's fragile health gave way and she was left alone to provide for their children, she fearlessly went out into the world to keep his name alive by playing his music in every capital of Europe. Indeed, were it not for Clara, it is very likely that much of the music of Robert Schumann might still be buried and forgotten.

And because she made it the business of her life to live for him, she too is not forgotten. Through her labors and her endless devotion, she fulfilled her husband's greatest dream— ". . . that posterity may regard us as one heart and one soul and may not know which is yours and which is mine."

HILDA WHITE

SONG WITHOUT END

The Love Story of Clara and Robert Schumann

PART ONE

THE INNOCENT YEARS

ONE

EVERYTHING was prepared for the journey. The boxes, marked and tied, were already being carried down the stairs by the servants. Displaying a handsome pair of satiny, impatient horses, the hired carriage stood waiting at the gate. In the brisk September wind, Alwin and Gustav, Clara's fledgling brothers, who were to be left behind, hung at the heels of the colorfully frocked driver, devouring with envious eyes every movement of the little procession of baggage carriers as they unloaded their burdens to the racks. Uncapped and without coats, dressed only in knee pants, purple vests and bow ties, the two boys ran back and forth inspecting everything, getting underfoot, and sharing a mutual thrill at the coarse tongue of their splendid coachman hero as he shouted insults now at them, now at the harassed servants.

What commotion! From an upstairs window, Clara's nurse, Nanny, who had been put in charge and who was not used to the responsibility, berated her fellow servants with a fervor almost equal to the driver's as from under her enormous black traveling hat, she kept a frantic eye on the more fragile of her mistress' packages. Her shrill cries attracted the attention of a few curious pedestrians who slowed their pace in the hope of witnessing a drama.

Other lively sounds blended in, sounds still more indigenous to *Grimmaischegasse*, the narrow, busy thoroughfare on which the music master's house stood: carriage wheels and horses' hoofs pounding by on the cobbled road; peddlers' carts jangling harsh little bells; the cathedral clock evenly striking the noon, summoning to the sunny street almost at once a throng of chattering clerks, schoolboys and laborers—all making a kind of appropriate symphony for this occasion. Herr Wieck and his daughter were setting off on a concert tour.

Eventually the boxes were successfully stacked, Nanny withdrew her handsome head from the window, and the driver, as haughty as a self-centered actor who chooses to ignore the stares of his admirers, mounted to his post, taking the reins.

Instantly the sensitive horses stomped, sniffed at the smoky Leipzig air, and raised their royal heads readying for the moment of departure.

"Where to? Where's your Papa off to now with the girl?" cried one of the less inhibited members of the little crowd which had collected.

Released from their trance, the two boys gleefully took over the stage. "To Paris! To Paris!" they shouted, jumping up and down with all the energy of their pent-up excitement. "Clara's going to Paris!"

And then, as if alarmed at their own uninhibited response to strangers, they vanished into the house like leaping hares, leaving their expectant audience still gaping.

For a brief time the onlookers refused to stir from their choice spots, unwilling to depart until the travelers had taken their places, until the driver uttered his rousing, spanking oath, and the dust flew at last into their faces.

But the neat little door, bearing upon it this informative inscription:

Herr Friedrich Wieck
Piano Instruction
Musical Instruments & Books for Hire

remained mysteriously closed. Everything, it seemed, was in readiness except the travelers themselves.

What was the cause of the delay? Was not the music master noted for his strict punctuality? Time passed. The noon hour was gone and the stream of clerks and schoolboys filed back behind the stone gates of their respective prisons. Only the driver, shifting and muttering, allowing his beasts to feel the flick of his anger, was left to watch and wonder.

None was to know then what bit of family drama it was which held up by some half-hour the start of this September journey. But there would come a day when the music master's house, destined as it was for fame, would empty all its secrets. On another day's noon in another year, the battle cry of love itself would fling open that tightly closed door, exposing for all the world to see the bitter and the sweet that lay within. The seed of that time was being planted even now, wanting only the slowly rising crescendo of life itself to burst the pod and ripen the fruit.

TWO

Early in the morning on the fifteenth of February in 1832 a stagecoach was making its way slowly, almost painfully, toward the beckoning steeples of Paris. A gray speckled sky, the groaning of wheels in the mud, and weariness from four long days and nights of travel had long since dispirited its passengers. A gloomy quiet settled over them, each sunk in thoughts of what lay ahead. For a long while, except for the creaking, turning disharmony of the sorely tried joints of the old coach, there was no communicative sound.

But it came soon—one word, casually caught from a passing peddler who rode by on his donkey. Cholera!

The listless group stirred. Anxious voices began to murmur. Some among them had fled their native German towns in the wake of the dread disease. Were they now to meet this deadly enemy in the very place they sought their refuge?

A middle-aged woman, bonneted, round-faced, with gray ringlets touching her rough cheeks, instinctively put her arm around the young girl who dozed beside her.

"Ach!" she whispered anxiously to the tall, stern-faced man sitting opposite. "You see! Frau Wieck was right. We should not have come. God knows what misfortune will befall."

"Hold your tongue, woman," came the man's icy reply. "There is no cholera, only fear of it."

He leaned back, tapping his fingers in quick staccato fashion on his portmanteau, the muscles of his cheeks working in angry spasms. How dare this foolish, gossiping old servant throw his wife's name into his face at such a moment?

Yet her words came like a sharp slap against his conscience.

"Take care, do you hear?" he warned, pointing to his sleeping child. "Not a word of this to Clara. She must be calm in Paris, *absolutely* calm. Everything depends upon it."

"*Ja, ja,*" nodded the nurse in a dull chant. But her tone was more lullaby for her young charge than agreement with the father.

The girl stirred. "Is anything the matter, Nanny?" she asked in a voice rich with sleep. "Will we be in Paris soon?"

"Soon, Clärchen," Herr Wieck said gently. "Sleep, sleep, my child."

When she had once more begun to doze, resting her head willingly against the comforting warmth of Nanny's arm, the indulgent father fastened his eyes with pride upon her young face. She was a pretty child, his Clara, with her lustrous dark hair, pale skin, and large, almost black eyes. She had not shown such promise her first few years. But now, at the approach of her thirteenth birthday, there was no longer any doubt. She was truly the ugly duckling turned swan.

But what pleased him even more was the quality of depth which a childhood enriched with musical culture had added to the expressive face. Yes, the child was unquestionably a treasure.

Involuntarily the face of Marianne Bargiel came into his mind. He had not thought about her for a long time now, and it surprised him that at this moment, after so many years, he could still think of her with such bitterness. Ah, but with a feeling of triumph too. Impulsive girl! She had dealt a blow to his pride by running off and deserting him, but he had

made her pay. How unwillingly she had complied with his
order (was it not the Saxon law?) to return their child, Clara,
on the little girl's fifth birthday. What tears and protestations!
Had he no heart to tear a child from her mother's arms?

His mouth quivered now into a contemplative smile. If he
had followed his original plan for this tour and gone to Berlin,
it would have pleased him immensely to display Clara before
that proud Frau Bargiel. He would have enjoyed showing off
to that lady what he had accomplished with the homely,
tongue-tied mite of a girl she had left so reluctantly in his
care. Now, thanks to him, and him alone, Clara was headed
for certain recognition and fame. By sheer persistence and
patience, deaf to all her mother's hysterical pleas to let the
child alone, he had, after all, with no ill effects on Clara,
cultivated in her a precosity on the piano which would soon
startle Paris as it had already startled her native Saxony.
Under his molding fingertips she had become an image of *his*
creativity. And now, now at last she was more than ready for
exhibition.

Ignoring the attempts of the other passengers to woo him
into their panicky and speculative chatter, the music master
turned his eyes upon the pearly cast of the February sky.
What a tedious journey! What dreadful luck they had had
with weather. And now this distressing talk of cholera.

For a single unguarded moment, a cold chill of fear pos-
sessed him. What if Clara *were* to be stricken? He could still
hear Clementine's frenzied words: "It is unthinkable, Friedrich, for you to take Clara on such a long journey now. Why,
cholera may kill that child!"

Clementine, whom—four years before—he had taken as his
second wife, although she was twenty years his junior, was
a sensible young woman, seldom interfering in his affairs. On

this occasion, however, she had allowed herself to become unreasonably hysterical after a visit from one of his pupils, Robert Schumann, who had come rushing into the house, newspaper in hand, to report that seventeen persons had caught cholera in Berlin, fourteen of whom had died, and three still in the doctors' hands.

Like a ghost shrouded in folds of black, the word cholera usually struck terror wherever it was mentioned. From time to time the disease swept in upon German cities, mercilessly taking all in its path. Mere rumors of its approach were almost as devastating, emptying a town quickly of all those fortunate enough to be able to flee. Although Berlin was far to the north, young Schumann was seriously talking of escaping to the safety of Zwickau, his home town. He had completely captured Clementine's imagination on this unfortunate subject.

"Who knows where cholera will strike next?" Wieck had ridiculed them both. "Shall we stop breathing, then? Shall we run and pull the covers over our heads?"

Not make the tour! Why, Paris had been his dream ever since Clara, at the tender age of eight, had first sat upon a platform and sped her skillful little fingers through a Mozart concerto. This was the opportune moment, now while she was still a little girl. Did not people always come out to hear a *Wunderkind*? The French capital was already welcoming other young artists—Felix Mendelssohn, Frédéric Chopin, and Czerny's remarkable pupil, Franz Liszt—virtuosos all. Among these names, he burned to plant another: Clara Wieck!

Wieck returned his gaze to Clara's drooping head, her full lips slightly parted, her long black lashes touching the roundness of her cheeks. How peacefully she slept. How foolish of him, even for a moment, to have succumbed to fear. What could possibly harm such a child?

Such care as he had lavished to develop Clara's mind, to guarantee her health, to perfect her musical training—surely God saw all and was pleased. After all, was it not through His divine inspiration that the name Clara had been chosen in the first place? *Illustrious* she was. Illustrious she would always be. It was her destiny.

THREE

Suddenly the carriage jolted to a stop. They had at last reached the first post inn in the suburbs of Paris. Instantly there was a bustle of confusion. Boxes were being handed down. Beggars pressed around the newcomers. And to Clara's ears, as she finally became aware of the completion of their journey, there came a babble of sounds as French and German intermingled in commands, shouts and insults.

Wieck, the first of the passengers to step out into the cold welcome Paris morning, quickly disappeared into the crowd leaving Nanny to manage alone the removal of their parcels. Muttering and complaining, she was soon engaged in a heated dispute with the driver over the apparent loss of a hatbox while Clara stood to the side, examining with lonely curiosity the scene about her.

This was certainly unlike anything she had ever experienced in her travels in Germany. There she was accustomed to strict orderliness. The authorities did not permit beggars to accost travelers at the post inns. But here there was almost a riot. A group of children dressed in little more than rags despite the severe weather immediately surrounded her, chattering and clamoring in high, intense voices. She knew only a smattering of French, having studied it for the first time a few months ago in preparation for this journey. But she did not need to know the language at all to be able to translate the hunger cry in their over-bright eyes as they came at her with their

thin little bodies and wasted faces. One child, frightfully
dirty, a boy of about six or seven, suddenly and without warning made a grab for her purse. Instinctively she drew back,
crying out, "No! No!" but a moment later she flushed with
shame as Nanny, rushing to the rescue, drove off the children
with a wave of her arms.

"Dirty! Diseased! Be off!" she screamed in frantic German.

This time it was the terrified children who needed no trans-
lation. They understood only too well the meaning of those
familiar gestures of rejection. Their cold and hunger would
not be alleviated here. Watching their swift dispersal, as if
afraid of being beaten, Clara, safe now under Nanny's fanati-
cally devoted eye, wondered what it was like to be such miserable creatures. She felt somehow personally responsible for
their plight.

"Thank God! There comes your father," Nanny said
breathlessly, pointing in the direction of the inn door.

Following her gaze, Clara too was immensely relieved to see
that dependable figure whose presence always seemed to her
to bring the world back into reassuring order. He was accompanied by a young man dressed in a long, square-cut coat,
loosely fitted, falling almost to his heels. The face under the
black hat was unfamiliar.

"It is Herr Fechner, your stepmother's brother," Nanny informed her. "Thank God we are so fortunate. He will see us
safely to our rooms." Nanny's brief encounter with the
"savages" of Paris had already assured her that she would not
be safe again until a solid German arm was on either side of
her.

Eduard Fechner was an aspiring artist who had deserted his
native Germany in favor of the excitement of Paris' art
circles. As he bent over to kiss Clara's small gloved hand,

however, his air of stiff formality was strongly reminiscent of a cautious German businessman. Yet, sitting beside him later in the *fiacre* and listening to his precise, rather high-pitched voice in conversation with her father, Clara's eyes began to twinkle in amusement. He seemed, in his outlandish redingote, a bundle of pretenses and affectation, not yet sure which would impress them most, his well-taught German manners or his newly acquired French bohemianism.

At this moment he was almost childishly delighted at being able to play the escort, pointing out as they plunged through the morning mist the Luxembourg, the great Notre Dame Cathedral and one of Paris' three magnificent opera houses.

"You must not fail to see Marie Dorval play Dumas at the Odeon," he said with a smile to Herr Wieck. "All Paris is in love with the ravishing girl. At the Théâtre Français there is Victor Hugo's new play. . . ."

But Wieck lent only half an ear to Eduard's chattering. He was impatient to get settled into his new quarters, for his head was already buzzing with plans of his own. "How far is it now?" he rudely cut in.

"Wait! we will soon be there," was Eduard's cheerful reply. "I found nice, but not too expensive, rooms in the Montmartre quarter on the rue de Bergère. We were lucky to find anything at all. Things are very dear in Paris today—three hundred *francs* a year for an attic! Oh, look, Clara," he interrupted himself excitedly, "there is Madame Wilhelmine Schroeder-Devrient going by in her carriage. What? You don't know her? Madame is *the* most exquisite artist at the Opéra. She was a favorite of the great Beethoven, you know."

Clara made haste to look, but caught only a glimpse of Madame's feathered bonnet as her hooded carriage sped by.

They now came into a section of the city which filled Clara

with wonderment. Squalor and poverty! It was everywhere. "So many beggars!" she said, frowning. "Is Paris full of them, Uncle Eduard?"

"Beggars and aristocrats! But citizens, all!" he said, gratefully pouncing on her question. "There you have Paris since the July uprising." His eyes lit up with shameless enthusiasm. "You are here for the first time, dear Clara. You don't know yet this incredible city. But I will show you everything. Paris! Crowded, noisy, dirty—but magnificent. Soon you will not be able to get enough of her blue mist, the river, the cathedrals!" He blew a kiss outward toward the clattering sounds of morning. "Sometimes you must sit in the café with me and hear how the students jabber about our citizen-king, Louis Phillipe. There will, of course, be another revolution."

At his last words Nanny rolled her head, striking her cheeks in horror! Cholera! Revolutions! What next? Herr Wieck threw his loquacious relative a warning frown, but the good-natured Eduard could see nothing in all the world about him to cause anyone dismay.

Clara suddenly broke into a warm smile. She, for one, was grateful for this artistic uncle of hers. Since leaving Leipzig she had traveled to Weimar, Erfurt, Gotha, Arnstadt, Cassel, Frankfurt am Main and Darmstadt; but not even her audience with the renowned Goethe, who with his skeleton fingers had propped a pillow beneath her so that she might more easily reach the keys of his piano, had roused in her the interest of these first few exciting moments in Paris. The discomforts, the fatigue of the long coach journey from the border, suddenly vanished. She looked now at Paris with shining eyes. At least it was no stuffy, slumbering city like some she had seen in Germany. It was alive and would furnish readable news for letters home to her brothers. Of Eduard she would write to Herr Schumann. He would be delighted to hear the opinions of a German artist in Paris, even one so ridiculously pretentious and affected as her amusing uncle. She settled back, already planning what she would say. The thought of Schumann had produced another kind of happiness inside of her. When they got back to Leipzig, he would be the first person she would like to see.

FOUR

Two HOURS after their arrival on the rue de Bergère, Clara was practicing the piano. Almost from the moment they had entered the small but adequate apartment Eduard had chosen, her father had impressed upon her that time was of the essence. Since they were foreigners in the French capital, he said, they would meet many more obstacles than in Germany, where at least his reputation as a teacher was already well-known. Here, too, the competition was keener, for Paris was literally engulfed in music, according to all reports.

He quickly made an inspection of the piano, an impressive-looking instrument of cherry-wood body which took up half the sitting room, declared it satisfactory, and produced for her to practice a set of variations on a theme of Mozart's composed by the young Polish virtuoso, Frédéric Chopin. He was anxious, for more than one reason, that she become expert with this new music.

Fixing his pale blue eyes hard upon hers, as if with them to drive home his point, his voice unconsciously took on something of a confidential whisper. "What luck that Chopin is in Paris! As soon as possible, Clara, he must hear you play his composition. If he is pleased—and why not?—perhaps he will introduce us to important people. In Paris that is the only way to get ahead—find favor with the aristocrats and play for them in their salons." He rubbed his hands. "So don't idle away your time, child. Practice! Practice as never before!

You'll see. Everything will be splendid—splendid!" And with this, he hurriedly took up his hat and went off, with the eager Eduard as a guide, to set into motion some of his elaborate plans.

For half an hour Clara obediently and diligently worked over the music. The feverish excitement for Paris which had grown upon her as they traveled along the boulevards in the *fiacre* made her impatient to go out onto the streets. The sound of hawkers and peddlers under her window was more enticing at this moment than the melodies of Chopin. Also, she was unused to the oversized piano. Its action was far too heavy and she was having difficulty making it obey the demands of the music.

At last, in frustration, she gave the keys an ill-tempered bang, and went to sit at the narrow little window where she was soon fascinated by the varied colors and motion of the street scene below. More of an alleyway than a street, its hum of crowded activity was like some constant song of life, one unfamiliar and distant to her own world but more enticing. An atmosphere of mystery was lent, too, by shafts of sunlight which plunged down at odd angles, creating, in contrast, pools of rising dust through which the bright colors of the ladies' hats bobbing back and forth were like tempting, forbidden fruit.

How she longed to escape, to run freely down to explore the odd little shops she saw and to mingle with all those gesticulating women who were pleading for bargains from the peddlers. She could be gone and back before her father returned—

Her mind moved, but her body remained obstinately still. Nanny, already busy baking in the kitchen, was there precisely to oversee her; an even stronger deterrent, however, was her own sense of discipline. Out of long habit it nipped in

the bud any such delinquent temptation. Yet, how much
fun it would be! Not once during these five long months
away from Leipzig had there been anything she so much
wanted to do. And she was capriciously in need of freedom,
of pure, unobserved relaxation!

Traveling in winter was never easy, and the constant strain
of preparing to perform in public robbed her of whatever
pleasure there was in visiting the various celebrities before
whom she had to play. Not that she blamed anyone. After
all, that was the life of a piano virtuoso.

Once at a Leipzig musicale she had overheard the conversation of two well-meaning old ladies who were not aware
that she sat just behind them. One of them remarked to the
other that Herr Wieck worked his daughter harder than a
child ought to be allowed to work. "It's a disgrace," replied
the other, "and something ought to be done about it. Why,
according to my information, the poor little girl has no time
at all to herself. No wonder she's extraordinary at the piano—
but she will be stunted in other ways."

Such slander against her father had astonished her. It was
true that he was firm, for he had little patience with indifference or laziness. But he was by no means a tyrant. It was
his method to teach her first to *hear* music as it ought to be
played, after which she was seldom satisfied to come to him
unprepared. He did not have to stand over her with a stick.
She worked hard because she was anxious to achieve high
standards. From the very first he had fired her imagination.
She had never wanted to be anything else except what he
wanted her to be—a great pianist. Of course it meant she had
to make sacrifices—

"But so many sacrifices—" she said discontentedly now to
herself.

She began to drum on the window sill, her lashes blinking

rapidly as they sometimes did when she was eager or impatient. She could hear Nanny in the kitchen singing an old German folk tune as she worked at her baking. Such was Nanny's way of comforting herself whenever she was far from home. Her voice was harsh but with that kind of gruffness which has a beauty of its own, especially when it is familiar and one has known it since earliest childhood. Dear Nanny, she too made sacrifices—

The singing, the scent of the sweet bread rising—how they made one think of home! What were her brothers doing this very moment? And Herr Schumann? Ah, if *he* were here, he'd soon make her stop feeling sorry for herself. His was a voice which could always bring a smile.

Turning her back on the tempting scene below, Clara resourcefully sought out her own bit of comfort in this lonely time. She took out a carefully preserved letter, one which had arrived when they were still in Frankfurt, and settled herself down to read it as she had done many times before during this long tour.

. . . So, dear Clara! I think often of you, not as a brother of his sister, or a friend of his friend, but rather as a pilgrim thinks of the picture over the altar far away. I have been in Arabia during your absence (how he liked to tease) so that I shall be able to relate all the fairy tales which might appeal to you—six new stories of phantom doubles, 101 charades, eight funny riddles, as well as some lovely, horrible robber stories, and that one about the white ghost—ugh! How I am trembling! Alwin has grown into a real young man; his new blue coat and leather cap, just like mine, become him very well. Of Gustav there is little to tell that is astonishing, except that he has grown so prodigiously that he is almost my size. . . . Alwin will probably keep at his violin. Have you been composing? And what? I have come to three-part fugues with Dorn. (Herr Dorn was teaching Schumann theory.) Be-

sides this a *Sonata in B minor* and a book of *Papillons* are ready;
the latter is to appear in print in two weeks. The weather is fine
today. How do the apples taste in Frankfurt? And how about
those three high F's in the *Variations* of Chopin? This sheet is
coming to an end; all things come to an end, except the friendship
in which I remain always Fräulein C. W.'s warmest admirer—

> (signed) R. Schumann

She had seen Robert Schumann for the first time when she
was eight years old. He was then seventeen and a law student
at Leipzig University. His presence, the tall, lean figure with
the persuasively friendly eyes and shock of brown hair falling
forward on his wide brow, had made a deep impression upon
her even at that time. Curiously, despite her instant accept-
ance of the friendship he offered in his warm gaze, she had
been like a rabbit who leaps into the grass, peering from a
distance, yet caught in the spell of the pursuer. He had not
been perplexed by her shyness: he threw her a look of sympathetic recognition which said clearly *Do not mistake me. I
am myself half-child. I know how it is, Clara.*

And when next he came to her home, proclaiming at length
to her father that one day he would give up law for music,
then afterward he proved to her the gentle strength of his
hands as he lifted her high into the air, showing her the depth
of kindness in his dark blue eyes, and the musical tones of
his laughter when she struggled to be free. Neither had had
to say in words then that which was already evident: age
made no difference between them; they were friends.

Clara sat for a long time over the treasured letter, longer
than she was aware, for she suddenly heard footsteps in the
hall, and realized with dismay that it was probably her father
already returning. And she with only one half-hour of practice
to report! In her haste to put Schumann's distracting letter

out of sight, it fell to the floor, landing at the feet of Eduard just as he came gaily sailing into the room.

"Aha! She blushes, our Clara," he said with a grin as he bent over to rescue the letter. "Have you secrets, *Liebchen?* A beau, perhaps?" There were teasing lights in his eyes.

Clara gave an embarrassed glance toward her father who was busy stripping off a pair of newly acquired French gloves. "Don't be silly, Uncle Eduard," she said, quickly taking the letter from his hands.

"Seriously, Clara! It is charming that you blush," her uncle went heedlessly on. "Parisian women are much too worldly. Still, who would have thought you, with your innocent eyes, old enough for love letters. No, don't protest," he insisted, shaking his finger at her, "when a young girl grows red and flustered over a letter, you can be sure she has something on her mind. . . ."

"Letter?" Wieck said, coming forward. "What letter is that, Clara?"

It would not have occurred before to Clara to keep secret from her father the fact that she was saving Schumann's letters. But Uncle Eduard's unfortunate teasing made her unwilling now to say whom the letter was from. Fortunately Nanny came to her rescue by bringing in a tray of coffee and her fresh-baked German cakes, the sight of which broke every other train of thought in the irrepressible Eduard.

"Ah! And what have we here?" he cried, leaping forward. The next moment he was licking his fingers and declaring to Nanny what marvelous memories of childhood her cooking brought to mind.

Over these bubbling sounds, Wieck made an attempt to describe to Clara his experiences of the afternoon. "We've had our first try at lining up a hall for your concert," he said. "What puffed up monsters these French managers are. 'Who?

Who? Clara Wieck?' No, they haven't heard of you *yet*.
'But, monsieur, our dates are all scheduled for a long, long
time. No, not an opening for months. Besides, you must
bring us certain guarantees—a name artist to draw in the
crowds—' All of them had the same sly tale."

A touch of wounded pride was discernible on his thin mouth
as he pursed his lips together over his coffee cup.

"I didn't know you were expecting me to play the concert
so soon anyway, Father," Clara said, wondering at his tone
of impatience. "Haven't we time?"

"Not for playing games with these fellows. Never mind.
They don't know with whom they deal. I went also to M.
Pleyel, of the piano firm. He tells me in confidence that
Kalkbrenner has entree to a certain Princess Vandamore. Her
salon is as good a place as any to make a start. So, Clärchen!
Tomorrow evening we go to Kalkbrenner's concert. Let us see
whom else we meet there. . . ."

Berlin-born Friedrich Wilhelm Kalkbrenner, Clara knew,
was Germany's outstanding pianist living in Paris. His concerts were always a great attraction, and she was thrilled to
realize that she was at last to hear him play. For her this was
motive enough for going. Her father's other devious maneuvers to win an audience for her were much too complicated
for her to follow.

"You may even be fortunate enough to see Mendelssohn
at the concert," Eduard put in between bites, joining their
conversation. "Do you know Parisians are more in love with
him than with Chopin? But then, being a banker's son has
its advantages. Chopin, they say, is better to look at. Still,
his revolutionary ideas won't make him popular with ladies
like the princess. Ah! she has the grandest soirees in Paris."

"Have you been to her, Uncle Eduard?"

"I? My dear Clara! I, the scum of Paris, a poor German painter not fit to walk on her rugs!" He laughed. "No such luck. But I hear the gossip in the cafés. She entertains only princes, ambassadors and ministers—plus a musician or two of renown." His eyes twinkled meaningfully in her direction.

"So! We shall find a way in," Wieck said confidently, wiping his mouth. "We did not come all this way to Paris for nothing." He turned abruptly to Clara. "Why were you not practicing when we returned? I thought I left you at the *Variations*. . . ."

"The piano!" Clara said, jumping up to demonstrate. "Listen, Father! The pedal is already sticking."

"We haven't *time* to worry about sticking pedals," he said reproachfully. "Were you asleep when I was explaining my plans—from whom was that letter you were reading when we came in?"

"Only Herr Schumann, Father."

"Oh." He smiled thinly. "That dreamer."

"Schumann? Schumann? Who is that?" Eduard demanded. "Can it be Clara's sweetheart?"

"I don't like to be teased, Uncle Eduard," Clara said with a warning frown. "Herr Schumann is Father's pupil who has been boarding with us. He's almost a member of the family—"

"Ah! a fellow musician. All the better," Eduard was laughing at Clara's angry eyes. "Is he also a *Wunderkind*, this Schumann?"

"Who knows what Schumann is," Wieck said darkly, his mood having become suddenly quite irritable. "I shan't waste much more time on him if he doesn't settle down. One would think that at the age of twenty-one he could be counted on. One moment he will be a virtuoso second to none—the next he is missing lessons to spend all his time composing. But he must be a composer by his own rules, mind you. I'll wager a guess he's complaining this very minute to Dorn that 'too much theory' will hamper his freedom—"

Clara followed his every word, all the while shaking her head in dispute. "But then he *can* be both, can't he, Father —a virtuoso and a composer? You should hear, Uncle Eduard, how beautifully he improvises!"

Wieck pushed back his chair. "We have no time either to be jabbering about Schumann. He has already caused enough mischief by taking your mind off your work today. Herr Fechner, you must excuse us, please. Good piano or bad, Clara must practice."

The amiable Eduard made a smiling bow in Clara's direction. "I see! For the sake of art, then, I forego the pleasure of your company, Clara." He took up his hat and coat. "Well, *Liebchen,* when your ogre releases you for a little while from your dungeon, you must come down to me. I'll take you strolling on the boulevard. *Oui?*"

Despite herself, Clara laughed merrily. "I'd like that very much, Uncle Eduard."

"*Auf Wiedersehen,* then," he said, jauntily putting on his hat. He sauntered from the room, and Clara, as she settled down beside her father for two hours of concentrated practice, thought he was taking away with him something of the spirit of Paris.

FIVE

THERE FOLLOWED exciting days of constant concert-going. But Wieck's plans for introducing Clara to discriminating music audiences were meeting with little success. Parisians with their hearth already richly warm with talent showed no impatience to hear a twelve-year-old *Fräulein* whose most vocal champion was her own effusive father. Kalkbrenner, a busy man, temporarily put Wieck off and Wieck did not take the slight with good humor.

For the first time that she could remember Clara saw her beloved parent in a frenzy of ill-tempered nervousness. It was almost as if a star he was pursuing elusively disappeared each time he reached out to put his fingers upon it. From early in the morning until late at night he kept running, his pace growing ever faster, to beg favors from influential people. Where was the "name-star" who would agree to appear at the debut of Clara Wieck? Where was the manager who would find an opening before the season closed? Who would help Clara find an entree to the salon of a wealthy patron? Vague promises were not enough and that was all he was hearing.

On the twenty-sixth of February young Chopin was scheduled to make his debut at Pleyel's. According to the announcements both Kalkbrenner and Mendelssohn were also to participate. This looked to Wieck a golden opportunity to catch all three stars in his net at once.

Meanwhile, a few days before that event, attired under

Eduard's influence in a smart blue tailcoat with velvet collar
and black, close-fitting trousers, Wieck took Clara to the
opera. Giacomo Meyerbeer's *Robert le Diable*, which was
then having a great success with the public, was being performed. Wieck had no great interest in Meyerbeer, for he
was in agreement with the exiled German poet, Heinrich
Heine, who called Meyerbeer a "worried genius catering to
the multitude, flattering the caprices of his public." Conse-
quently, he concentrated the greater part of his attention on
all the possible patrons he could find in the audience, his blue
eyes darting greedily from box to box.

Clara too was gaily decked out for the occasion. She was
wearing a dark velvet ribbon wound about the braided coils
piled atop her head. Her new gown was of white satin falling
gracefully away from her shoulders, the sleeves puffed into
billowing folds of softness which gradually tapered off to a
fitted wrist. Around her neck was a gold band given to her
that day by her father, and she was wearing earrings for the
first time. Eduard had assured her that she must be fashionable among Parisian women. All around her, in the dazzling
opera house, she saw white-gloved hands holding jeweled
binoculars, and daring costumes generously adorned with
diamonds and exquisite pearls. What a contrast to the bleak
scene which had greeted her the day of her arrival in Paris.

The opera itself Clara found fascinating. It was a strange
story of a man seeking to find saintliness but unable to resist
the temptations of the devil. Mademoiselle Falcon, who was
to have sung the leading role, was replaced at this performance
by Madame Schroeder-Devrient, of whom Eduard had spoken
so highly. Her exquisite voice made a deep impression upon
Clara. At one point, as she closed her eyes listening in rapt
attention to the faultlessly clear soprano tone, it made her
think of Paganini's violin. Two years ago, through her father's

persuasion, the great Italian violinist had come to Leipzig, and she could still remember how he had made of his singing instrument an almost human voice—a voice as pure as Madame's. She had been privileged to play for him, with her father, a four-handed arrangement of a rondo on themes from Paganini. In her album that day he had written: *al merito singulare di Madamigella Clara Wieck.*

Now Wieck leaned forward and whispered that he would take her backstage after the opera to meet Schroeder-Devrient. Although he did not know it at the moment, it was to prove a most fortunate proposal.

No sooner had the curtain fallen than he made his way with her through the vast crowds, reaching the wings at the very moment when Madame was being burdened with flowers from a group of her admirers. Despite their prior claims, Wieck deftly pushed Clara through until suddenly she was the center of attention.

"Clara Wieck? Oh, yes! Indeed I have heard of you, Fräulein," said the singer, "and from none other than Paganini himself. Do you know that he is in Paris? 'The dear little girl,' he said to me, 'plays the piano like an angel.'"

Clara was astonished at the coincidence of this mention of Paganini when she had only now been thinking of him. She stood speechless, staring. But Wieck, barely able to restrain his excitement at the news, filled in for her. "I hope," he said, beaming, "Madame will do us the honor of attending Clara's Paris debut."

Schroeder-Devrient inquired the date and place of that event. Wieck, unflustered, replied that due to certain difficulties (which he hoped to overcome almost immediately!) the time had not yet been set.

"Ah! So!" she replied graciously. "Then you must let me know. And if I can be of any help, call on me. . . ."

"We are in luck!" Wieck said gleefully as soon as they were again on the street. "Paganini in Paris! His name is worth gold, Clara. We will not need the help now of Madame, or anyone else for that matter, for I am certain *he* will agree to sponsor your concert. Soon we will show these haughty Parisians what a German girl is capable of!"

The following morning he rose early and went to call upon the violinist, but was told that Paganini was indisposed and receiving no callers. Disappointed, Wieck left his card. Later in the day, however, a messenger arrived with an invitation for Clara and her father to pay the maestro a visit the following week.

Thus, with a lighter heart than he had yet had in Paris, Wieck went on the twenty-sixth with Clara to No. 9 rue Cadet, the salons of M. Pleyel, which was to be the scene of Chopin's debut. Kalkbrenner, of whom Chopin was rumored to have said, "He is one whose shoelace I am not worthy to untie," had himself made all the arrangements. He had included on the program his own *Grand Polonaise* and an *Introduction and March* composed for six pianos. For this latter number Chopin, Mendelssohn and the composer himself were to be featured. No wonder the salon was filled.

From the platform Chopin seemed so fragile with his delicately thin hands that it hardly seemed possible to Clara he would be able to bring tone from the piano. After the conclusion of a vocal duet executed by Mlles. Toméoni and Isambert, he came slowly forward and, without a glance at the audience, seated himself at the piano. As he began his *Concerto in F minor*, suddenly the hall seemed magically transformed, with the sparkling tones coming from some other world, from an instrument of unearthly perfection.

Was he real, this almost ethereal figure, whose music came

like poetry from the keys? Clara knew now why Schumann had been so enthusiastic about introducing him to the German public when he wrote in his review of Chopin's Opus 2, "Hats off, gentlemen! A genius!"

Coming after the delicate, web-like poem of Chopin's creation, Kalkbrenner's *March* seemed a rude intruder with its too grand style. Also, to the disappointment of the audience, Mendelssohn was not at one of the six pianos as promised. In his place sat a pupil of Kalkbrenner's, Camille-Marie Stamaty, a young man unknown at the time but one day to be noted as a great teacher.

Still, there was an air of unabated excitement in the hall, for Chopin had completely captured the imagination of the audience and it could not have enough of him. Clara listened closely to his playing of *La ci darem* for these were the variations on which she was working so hard. His ease, his grace, his deep feeling filled her with inspiration. When next she sat down to practice them, she thought, she would be able to trace with more certainty the composer's meaning.

During the reception which followed, everyone pressed forward to meet the fabulous young Pole. When Clara was able to get close enough, she stared at his pale face under the ash-blond hair as if to determine for herself that he was not an imaginary being. He must be at least Schumann's age, she thought. Kalkbrenner, who stood at Chopin's elbow, said to him with a smile, "Here is Fräulein Clara Wieck. If rumors be true, she may well be your rival as a virtuoso." Clara flushed, for Kalkbrenner was obviously making fun of her. Others in the room laughed at his remark, but Chopin seemed instantly to understand her feelings.

"Never mind, Fräulein. We shall speak together another time when there are not so many."

Had he really said those words? They were so softly spoken she could not be sure. The next moment she was swept away by her father to shake hands with M. Pleyel and two handsome young men standing side by side, the Hungarian pianist Franz Liszt and Germany's own Felix Mendelssohn.

Paris now received Chopin as one of its own. He was discussed everywhere. The Belgian music historian, François Joseph Fétis, wrote of his debut: "Here is a young man who gives way to his natural leanings and taking no model, has found, if not a way of revising piano music completely, at least some of what has so long been vainly sought—that is, an abundance of original ideas. M. Chopin is gifted with the power of a Beethoven. There is soul in his melodies, fantasy in his figuration, and originality in everything. His playing is elegant, facile, graceful and has brilliance and clarity."

Wieck was rejoicing. Clara's little episode with Chopin which had caused her so much embarrassment brought her an invitation to visit him in his rooms on the Boulevard Poissonnière. And at the debut he had maneuvered an invitation for them both to dine with the Kalkbrenners. This last affair, although it brought a definite guarantee that Clara was to play soon at one of Princess Vandamore's soirees, cost Wieck the unpleasant experience of being forced first to listen to a lengthy lecture from Madame Kalkbrenner on the poor quality of German piano teaching and her strong opinion that Clara should continue her musical training elsewhere. Wieck, under the circumstances, dared not explode to that lady that she had insulted *him*, Clara's teacher. He had to swallow his pride along with his dinner.

Praise of the most extravagant kind did not seem in the least to have turned Chopin's head. When Clara and Nanny were admitted to his rooms on the afternoon of her appointment, the young composer's easy smile soon overcame Clara's shyness. She played for him his Mozart *Variations* after which he exclaimed, "But Kalkbrenner is right. You *are* a fine pianist. I think one has to look out for you, Clara."

He then began to ply her with questions. When had she begun to study? Did she mind practicing? Did she suffer stage fright at her concerts?

She told him how, on her fifth birthday, her father had led her to the piano and told her the names of the notes. Each day thereafter he sat with her teaching her how to strengthen her fingers as well as how to listen for melody. " 'But the piano must *sing!*' he would scold if I chopped at the notes and forgot legato. 'Sing, sing, sing!' he would shout until it sometimes put me into tears. I understood him but my baby fingers would not behave. Then one day I could feel my hands gaining strength. I had control. Father was so proud. He would boast to everyone who came, 'Listen to my Clara play!' Now I must practice two hours instead of one, and as I grew older, three and four hours."

"What!" exclaimed Chopin. "Didn't you want to run out to play?"

"Oh, yes. And Father sometimes had to be stern, especially as I was then very stubborn. But he was right. He saw to it that I had plenty of time to be outdoors in good weather. 'One may have health without piano,' he used to say, 'but cannot have the piano without health.' "

"Tell me about your first concert."

Clara laughed. "It was in late October, 1828 when I had just turned nine years old. To play in the Gewandhaus was a great honor! I had a new dress and cape and everyone at home was making a fuss over me. As it was necessary for Father to be early at the hall to check the piano and other details, he left instructions that I was to wait in the vestibule at home until he sent the Gewandhaus coach to call for me. Soon I heard the tinkle of the horse bells and my stepmother rushed me out and put me into the coach. So there I was, my heart beating almost as fast as the horses' hoofs which were flying along in the dark. There were two or three other little girls in the coach which was surprising as Father had said I would be alone. They seemed equally surprised to see me, but as not one of them said a word, I remained very quiet. Suddenly I realized that something was wrong. The coach did not make a stop at the Gewandhaus but went speeding on toward the suburbs. It was already time for my concert to begin and here was I being carried away—by whom? Where? I was too proud to burst into tears before those strange little girls, but it was what I wanted to do. Poor Father, I was thinking. What he must be suffering back there at the Gewandhaus after all his hard work to prepare me. He had so looked forward to my debut."

Chopin laughed as she paused for breath. "Oh, but don't stop, Clara. I sit on the edge of my chair! Go on! Go on!"

"Just as we were nearing the little country place of Eurtritzsch there came the sound of another coach following after us at great speed. It turned out to be the Gewandhaus coach coming to my rescue. The coach in which I was riding was taking a group of little girls to a country dance. It had been instructed to pick up Clara, the porter's daughter at a house on Salt Lane which was where we lived at the time. It had simply picked up the wrong Clara."

"I see! And what did your father say to all this when you arrived so late for your debut?"

" 'I quite forgot to tell you, Clara, that everyone is carried off by strangers before playing for the first time in public!' "

She and Chopin laughed heartily. All formality between them was gone and they now took turns relating amusing adventures in their careers. When Clara finally had to part from him, she went away with the fullest realization that she had had the privilege of spending the afternoon with a great man.

SIX

FOR WIECK the sun was now shining and he could dash back and forth whistling with his chest puffed a little under his smart new vest. Paganini, the magnificent Paganini, had graciously consented to play at Clara's concert!

"So! Now what have you to say?" he shouted triumphantly to those concert managers who had snubbed him. "Was I right about Clara? Paganini himself indorses her!"

This was the great moment for which Wieck had so long been waiting. Clara and Paganini on the same program! Success was almost close enough to touch.

The Hôtel de Ville was booked for the ninth of April and he charged Eduard with the responsibility of getting the announcements printed and the tickets made ready. Meanwhile there was the soiree. A few select Parisians would have the privilege of hearing the *Wunderkind,* and once they spread the word about, people would flock to the Hôtel de Ville eager to hear Clara play.

It was the custom in Paris for pianists to perform from memory. As Clara was not used to this, she now spent what seemed interminable hours of hard practice in preparation for the soiree and her debut. Nanny was afraid she would break under the strain.

"My poor baby, my poor baby," she went around mumbling to herself.

But Wieck was obsessed with only one thing: the debut—

April ninth. "She is all right," he said to Nanny's grumbling. "She isn't complaining of anything. Only another few days and it will all be over. Then she can have a nice long rest."

A gray chill was in the air on the night they drove to the mansion of Princess Vandamore. With her hands inside her muff cold from nervousness, Clara sat listening not to the sound of the clattering wheels but to the strains of music in her memory. Would they fail her when her time came to perform? Tonight for the first time she would not have the reassurance of her father sitting beside her. She could not lean on his nearness, his whispered encouragement. And so much depended on her success. If she broke down—if her memory failed— She stole a glance at her father. His face wore a look of absolute confidence. *He* seemed so sure—so proud.

The chamber orchestra was playing when they arrived, and guests were dancing in the great hall. Servants in full livery went through the rooms serving food and champagne to those who did not choose to dance. Glasses and crystal chandeliers sparkled. Jewels were glistening and laughter was rising above the music.

For a long while Clara was left sitting in one corner of the ballroom while her father went off to find out at what hour she was expected to perform.

At such affairs as these, and there had been many similar ones during their tour in Germany, she often had the feeling that she would be forgotten. The moment her father was out of sight she was overcome with loneliness and uneasiness. She remembered other times when she had nearly fallen asleep waiting her turn to play. At the court in Cassel she had been kept waiting until midnight.

To raise her spirits she now began to hum the waltz the orchestra was playing and to imagine herself one of those carefree beautiful ladies swept along by a handsome partner. Oh, it was a burden sometimes to be a performer. How lighthearted she would feel now if her only task was to make cheerful conversation, and to dance well with her escort.

Rustling skirts circled dizzily past her. The music seemed to be playing much too fast for a waltz. The room was bathed with light, everyone in ecstatic motion except herself. She felt uncomfortably warm, and then suddenly cold as if a chill had come into the room. If only her father would come back—

All at once, as if in a dream, the dancers began to break away from one another. Little groups collected, whispering in corners. The orchestra exposed so mysteriously to an almost empty floor went on playing with a kind of urgent frenzy until one by one the strings paused in defeat. Clara stood up, puzzled, frightened. Some of the guests, as if in a great hurry, were putting on their wraps preparing to leave. She saw unmistakable panic written on their faces.

Thank goodness there was her father coming across the floor in her direction. Princess Vandamore was with him.

"My child," said the princess, taking her by the shoulders, "I depend on *you* now to save my party. Hurry! You must begin to play before all my guests leave. Hurry! Hurry! I will announce you myself."

Clara threw a puzzled plea for help to her father. He too looked like the others in the room, as if he were afraid. "Don't ask questions, Clara," he said, pushing her gently toward the piano. "Go! Do as you're told. And God be with us all."

Trembling with fear and uncertainty Clara sat down at the piano, hearing as if from a great distance the shrill voice of the princess announcing: "Your attention, everyone!

Please! Pay attention. We have now the honor of hearing Fräulein Clara Wieck—"

She could feel the arrested guests drawing closer, see from the corner of her eye only filmy shrouds of material from costly evening gowns. Where was her father? Her fingers were too cold to play. She could remember nothing.

A stern inner voice prompted her: *There is nothing to fear. Come, now. Everyone is waiting. Begin at once! Play! Play, Clara—*

Whispers ceased as she began. Someone was closing the great doors to the ballroom. She was no longer cold. And the most fantastic things seemed to be happening as her fingers obeyed the rigors of long training and performed. Surely that was Schumann's face smiling at her from behind the piano, his voice saying, *Bravo, little Clara! Bravo!* And there was Chopin standing beside him, smiling, his look of admiration saying, *One has to look out for you, Clara!*

At last! It was over. She turned about and saw a sea of strange faces staring at her, heard finally the delayed, enthusiastic applause. The princess was smiling at her gratefully. She could hear her father explaining, "But you will be able to hear Clara again—April ninth, Hôtel de Ville—"

They drove home through a dismal rain. Wieck did not speak, not even to give her praise. Clara saw with dismay that his face no longer wore the look of triumph with which he had arrived an hour earlier. He was so tense and drawn that she was frightened for him.

"What happened tonight, Father? Why was everyone so strange?"

He looked steadily at her for a moment, then turned away as if not to answer. But after a moment he said in a low voice, "One of the princess' servants was suddenly taken ill

and someone spread the word about that it was cholera.
But it was a rumor—only a rumor."

"Oh," said Clara, "then there was nothing to worry about
after all."

"No. Nothing to worry about at all. And you, Clara, you
did admirably, admirably—"

At peace again, Clara closed her eyes listening to the steady
downpour of rain. Cholera! What was it, anyway, to make
people so frightened . . . even her father, who was usually so
brave? She settled her head comfortably against the warmth
of his shoulder. As for her, as long as he was nearby, she always
felt safe. The rain, the horses' hoofbeats, the waltz to which
she had wanted to dance now began to blend into a confusion of sounds. Consumed by weariness, she fell asleep.

Wieck could not for long keep from Clara the truth of
what had happened. Rumor grew into incontestable facts.
Cholera was rampant in Paris. Mendelssohn was down with
it. And the most devastating blow—Paganini had taken to
his heels and fled.

By the end of the week people were deserting Paris in droves.
Wieck did not allow Clara to go out onto the streets, nor did
he urge her to practice. He himself went frantically about
trying to find another artist to replace Paganini. Eduard,
finally, suggested Madame Schroeder-Devrient. Wieck hurried
off to see her, recalling how sincerely she had once promised
him help if he needed it. If only she too were not set to flee.
To his relief she greeted him with more strength and courage
than he had seen exhibited by anyone else. No, she would
not leave Paris! Yes, she *would* replace Paganini.

"But I will give you advice," she said. "You must cancel the
Hôtel de Ville and take a smaller hall. Believe me, sir, it is
the best you can do. At times like these one cannot expect
a miracle—"

"You, Madame," he said, "are a miracle."

She smiled. "Try one of the music schools. And take the first date offered. I realize what a loss the printing of the tickets has already cost you, so you daren't take a chance again. Clara is well—I am well—who knows what tomorrow will bring?"

Her words chilled his heart, but he agreed. Now one could only make the best of this miserable situation. Put a brave face forward, allow Clara to play, and pray! But inwardly he no longer had enthusiasm for the concert. Every instinct told him that cholera was the victor after all. Streets were deserted. Funeral carts rattled below the windows. From nearby houses chants of sorrow wailed dismally.

"It is better we go home," was Nanny's constant cry.

Acting on the suggestion of Schroeder-Devrient, Wieck quickly secured a room in a music school while Eduard saw to the printing of new circulars. Both knew, but did not admit to one another, that these gestures were really worthless. The voice of fear was mistress of the day. To that voice and not to Devrient's would people listen.

But finally Clara's Paris debut did take place. The small hall they had taken in compromise was itself half-empty. Clara could see her father standing at the rear and knew from his drawn face that he was finally defeated.

If only she could repay him all his labor, all his devotion, all that the tour had cost him both in money and anxiety. But she could only give him what was in her fingers. Today she would play for him alone, never mind the others. Dear, dear Father, she thought, all is not lost. There will be other times. Listen! These fingers, so lovingly trained by you, *they* will be your reward. They will make up one day for everything. And she poured her thoughts into the music.

The following morning, through quiet streets, their coach

started the long journey homeward. Now Paris neither beckoned nor bid good-by. Here and there a lone hawker raised his shrill cry under unheeding windows. And along the way they saw gray figures of misery searching the mounds of uncollected debris for food. To these unfortunates the frightened aristocrats had willingly left their suffering city.

Clara was glad to leave it all behind. Only Eduard and Chopin had brought momentary joy, and even Eduard, as he saw them off, wore on his face not the gay mask of a Paris alive but one of a city at the mercy of death.

"*Ach!* Now it is good we go home," Nanny said with a deep sigh of relief as the horses sped along.

This time Herr Wieck had nothing to say.

SEVEN

DAYBREAK in Leipzig was a busy affair. It was not the cock's crow shaking up the world for duty, but rather the rattling of the peddlers' carts, the tinkle of the baker's bell, the creaking of the merchant's door as he pushed it back for business. Soon from the narrow streets mongrel dogs set up their barking, racing at the heels of the laborer as he hurried along to earn his daily bread. Industry was the rule in Leipzig. Mothers taught it to their daughters and fathers to their sons. It was the key unlocking the gates of morning.

At 641 Neumarkt there stood a house crowded in on either side by lofts and shops. It faced the busy thoroughfare, unpretentious in its plainness, but a model of that neat kind of residence which takes in to board students or transients who have something in their pockets to pay for a better kind of "rooming house." Here, two flights up and in a small room crowded by an immense piano, there slept on this May morning one who was blissfully unaware of bells, footsteps, hawkers' cries or the pounding of his landlady upon his door. If these sounds penetrated his dreams they merged into a kind of music which the dreamer's mind absorbs and transfers to suit purposes of its own in that nether world.

The shades of this small haven were drawn long after the light had lost its first paleness and grown into a full bloom of sun basking over the busy market place. For its young occupant, having applied his energy to a long night of controversial arguments dealing with politics, poetry, music and love, had parted late from his friends, coming from the dusky tavern only as the day began.

But in time a sound penetrated his dreams which struck a sympathetic chord, a sound strong enough under any circumstances to rouse his attention. It was the voice of a child.

"Herr Schumann! Wake up, up there! Herr Schumann!"

And a shower of pebbles hit against the closed pane.

In an instant the young man leaped from his bed and peered down to the bright street below. "So, you rascal! Is it only you waking me up?" He ran his fingers through his thick brown hair and shook himself, delighted with day now that he was awake. Oddly enough through the scent of bread and fowl, leather and horses, there came to his nostrils the odor of flowers. Leipzig might utilize every inch of the inner circle of the town for thriving business, but nature, not too far distant in Connewitz woods, was a powerful rival sending out her sharpest signals to tempt the inhabitants from their labor. Once awake, the young man's senses were attuned to all the impulses of life.

"Shame!" cried the child's high-pitched voice. Feet planted apart, he stood cross-armed, pretending to scold his friend for so wasting this beautiful day. But his eyes, shining with adoration, and his thin mouth, spreading into an irresistible grin, took off the edge of his criticism. "I have news!" he burst out in a pitch of excitement.

"I know your kind of news," said Schumann, laughing. "You've found a bird nest in the park and in it are three skinny little babies peeping their heads off for breakfast."

"Not birds!" exclaimed the boy impatiently. "It's Father. And Clara! They're back from Paris!"

"What!" Schumann let out a shout of unashamed pleasure.

"Good gracious, man. Why didn't you say so?" The next moment his shaggy head disappeared from the window.

The boy sat down on the step of the ugly little building to wait. He was slender, with a crop of yellow hair showing from under his cap, wearing blue jacket and short blue pants and a trim little bow tie at his neck. In his clean, spotless appearance there was not one sign betraying spring's mark on a boy; no shirttail escaping from the pants, no collar open at the neck, or pockets protruding with precious trophies. From head to toe he was as proper as his stepmother intended him to be. Yet before long there came to his pursed lips a song to whistle as he waited for his friend, and from within an inner pocket of his vest he mysteriously produced two marbles which he began to roll about in his fist. The exquisite smoothness of their surface and the purity of their glistening, brilliant colors fascinated him. There was, he thought, no creation of man's more marvelous than a marble.

At last the door behind him burst open and Schumann, somewhat disheveled in his haste, emerged. His cap was in his hand, his jacket unbuttoned, and his pocket bulged with something more obtrusive than a marble, this being a thickly rolled manuscript of music.

For all his twenty-one years, Robert Schumann, lean and quivering with intense love and enthusiasm for life, appeared to the eye of the passer-by this May day more boy than man. His stride was fast, his gaze everywhere at once, and it was hard to say at what he was smiling.

Alwin Wieck trotted along beside him keeping up an excited chatter. He was anxious to have the joy of being the first to tell as much of Clara's news as he could remember. But this ambition was almost futile for he had to keep at a breathless run to match the pace of the long-legged Schumann.

The Wiecks lived not far from the concert hall on Neumarkt. A carriage stood out front, its horses bending their
heads and doing a kind of stomping dance. The sweetness
of May was in their nostrils. Over them, over the modest,
trim gardens, over the roofs of all the dwellings, the sun
poured its sparkling glow. But the door of Frau Wieck's
house, according to her custom, was kept carefully closed
and little of the May warmth was allowed to creep into her
parlor. Of necessity, one always had to ring for admittance.
Not even Alwin with his rude vivacious energy was allowed
to push in without the summoning of a servant.

A prompt response to the bell, however, was another
characteristic sign of efficiency in Clementine's resourceful
household. Only a minute or two elapsed before Alwin was
racing ahead of Schumann up the steps, announcing in his
boyishly shrill voice that Herr Schumann had arrived.

"In a moment! Oh, Alwin, please tell him to wait only
one more moment!" Clara's voice rang out.

Schumann smiled at the girl's charged tone of excitement
and could envision her as he had seen her last, the deep brown
eyes brimming with sincerity as she bade him good-by. How
passionately intense she was, this dark-eyed Clara. How
possessively she treasured her family and friends.

The servant having disappeared into the pantry, Schumann
found himself for the moment alone. With the ease of other
days when he was still living in this house, he had impulsively
started up the steps until Clara's cry had stopped him. Now
he retreated, thinking to wait in the music room, but the
double doors were closed against him. Wieck must be there,
already at work. At this moment the smile faded from
Schumann's mouth, for only now did he remember how little
reason for joy there was in this reunion with his former

teacher. How many times during the past month he had visualized that terrible moment when Wieck would at last discover what had happened to him in his absence. Yet Alwin's news had sent him rushing headlong, the way a child rushes, heedless of danger.

Slowly he lifted his right hand and looked down at the awkward spread of his fingers, his face contorting strangely. "Here, master," he must say, "here is the hand you were training so carefully. I have damaged it, as you can see. There is no help for it. I'll never be a virtuoso now—never. I can be your pupil no longer."

Lost! Stupidly, blunderingly lost the opportunity to become in Wieck's own words "one of the greatest living pianists, playing with more imagination and warmth than Moscheles, more splendidly than Hummel. . . ."

With a groan Schumann thrust the wounded hand out of his vision, and thought, in this moment of panic, not of that which had blissfully come to serve as consolation—how through his gift for composing he had finer, more lasting treasures to offer the world—but of flight from the inevitable punishment of Wieck's reproachful eyes. Wieck was not like other men. He did not easily forgive those who betrayed the confidence he had put in them. His capacity for tolerance or compassion was limited. Now, for example, he would recognize not the zeal which had prompted his pupil into using a clumsy, self-constructed mechanical device meant to strengthen a weak fourth finger, but the folly, the foolishly shattered career—

Poor, stiff, dead little finger! Not it, nor its contrite owner stood much chance of receiving a word of pity from the proud, correct man who sat behind those paneled doors.

There were strong currents of cowardice charging through

Schumann. Tomorrow, he thought, that was time enough to let Wieck know—he would leave quickly now, and come back in the morning.

But as he put his hand to the knob of the outer door, Wieck himself came out of seclusion, and Schumann, trapped, swung around to see his teacher's welcoming smile.

"So! You are here already, Schumann! Well, come in! Come in, why don't you? Don't just stand there. Have you nothing to say to me after my long absence?"

The younger man grinned awkwardly, mumbling almost inaudibly that he was waiting for Clara and her brothers who had promised to come down any moment. . . .

"Well," said Wieck with undeniable logic, "they won't miss seeing you in the parlor. Let's have a word there together meanwhile."

Schumann allowed himself to be drawn in, his mind racing feverishly to find an excuse for quick withdrawal. "Wonderful to have you back in Leipzig, sir," he said in a dry voice. But he made no effort to offer his deformed hand in greeting.

Wieck, with folded arms, stood looking at his pupil through critical, inquisitive eyes. He seldom missed any detail. His curiosity encompassed everything. At a glance he almost always knew the color of a man's neckpiece, the price of his shoes, the approximate amount of his annual income. If he entered a house to which he had been invited for the first time, he usually could tell on leaving the number of closets it held, the size of the kitchen, the contents of the cupboards, the age of the rug on the floor. That there was something offensive as well as boorish in this prying behavior never seemed to occur to him. It was, by now, so much an appendage of his trade and indispensable, he thought, if one were to know all possibilities, that he had fitted it permanently into the pattern of his behavior. Wherever he went his eyes asked questions. Is there, by chance, a prospective patron here? A contact for Clara's future benefit? A promising pupil or a purchaser for a musical instrument?

His question now was: *What's troubling Schumann? It's my guess he is trying to hide something important from me.* Aloud, he said, "What good things have you to report of yourself during my absence, young man? What progress have you made with Dorn?"

"Progress?" Schumann repeated, almost stupidly. With difficulty he brought his distracted mind back to attention. "You will be pleased, sir. . . . I've brought something to show you. . . ." Nervously he drew out the bulging manuscript from his back pocket. "A composition—see for yourself. Already published!"

Adjusting his monocle, Wieck held at a distance the music which Schumann so proudly handed him. For what seemed to the composer an unbearably long time, he stared down at its title page.

Forgetting for the moment his other problems, Schumann could barely restrain his impatience. "I want very much to hear your opinion of it, sir," he suddenly burst forth.

Wieck felt inclined to play one of his dry little jokes. His mouth quivered into a mocking smile. *"Papillons!* So! You've taken now to composing butterfly music, eh, Schumann?"

Furious with disappointment, Schumann began to stammer his explanation of the composition's title, and Wieck let forth one of his rare bursts of laughter.

"Never mind!" he cried out, cruelly delighting in Schumann's confusion. "Play it for me now, and I will hear soon enough if it doesn't flutter about with delicate wings. Wait! I'll hurry Clara along to hear it too. She rather fancies these *dainty* pieces."

At any other time than this, Schumann might have shared
objectively his teacher's moment of fun. He knew full well
that they had always had a musical taste in common. Both
were great admirers of Schubert *Lieder* and of the genius of
Mozart; both had enthusiasm for reviving the masterpieces
of Leipzig's sadly neglected Johann Sebastian Bach. In the
realm of criticism at least the two were drawn together on
a plane of relationship uncommon in Wieck's usual code of
conduct with his pupils. It ought therefore to have been
plain enough to Schumann what Wieck was up to, but his
present mood was too subjective to stand the teasing. Besides,
being forced to play his composition would mean immediate
exposure of his deformed finger. No! This was all too much
to stand—the mockery of his music, the inevitable abuse
which would soon pour down upon him when Wieck saw the
permanently injured hand.

But escape seemed out of the question. Clara was already
on her way down. And with her the ingratiatingly polite
Clementine, accompanied by Alwin and Gustav. He was in
for it now—a recital before the entire family. He began to
tremble inwardly.

There was a ceremony of handshaking with Frau Wieck
before Clara was able to step finally into his full view. "See
how she's grown," Wieck's wife was saying, but Schumann
had ceased to hear her. He was experiencing, after his previous moments of panic, a sense of wonderful relief at sight
of Clara. Why was it that this curious little girl always
seemed to him like an island of safety for himself?

"Welcome! Welcome home, Clara," he said with genuine
emotion. His eyes took in her whole appearance. Had she
changed much these past months? In figure, yes, for when
he had seen her last she had had the slimness of a boy. Ah,

but the face! It had the same innocence, the same sweet lack of guile. She was, thank goodness, still a child. If only she could always stay the same—

"We have a treat in store for us, Clara," Wieck said, taking her by the arm. "We are no sooner home than Schumann brings us his latest composition."

"Yes! And I was the first to hear about it. Isn't it splendid?" Clementine said, rushing forward to remove the fringed rug which had covered the piano since her husband's absence. "His piece is published, Clara!"

"*Papillons?*" Clara inquired, smiling in Schumann's direction. She was not surprised, she informed her stepmother, for he had written her about it months ago.

Schumann was shaking his head and drawing back as Wieck beckoned him to the piano. "No, no," he insisted. "It was very awkward of me to come rushing in like this to spoil your family reunion." He put on his cap and held his hand out to Wieck for his composition. "I'll come another time—my music can wait."

"Nonsense!" Wieck shouted cheerfully. "In this household music comes before everything else." He placed the manuscript carefully on the rack and with a glance commanded the others in the room to settle themselves down in preparation for Schumann's performance. "Now, then! We are waiting," he said with a grin to Schumann, "for your butterfly dance to begin."

Clara meanwhile had been quick to notice that all was not right with Schumann. She thought he must be ill, especially as he now continued to stand motionless in the center of the room, a look of intense discomfort on his face.

Alwin, being a wise little fellow, had already guessed Schumann's difficulty, and gave a sudden tug at Clara's sleeve.

She leaned down to hear what it was he was whispering to her. A moment later she walked briskly toward the paralyzed Schumann.

"Would you permit *me* to play *Papillons* for my parents, Herr Schumann? Please! On my first day home, you won't refuse me the favor, will you?"

Inwardly she was suffering for him all the anguish he must be experiencing. *Schumann has hurt his finger,* Alwin had whispered, *and doesn't want Father to know it.* Of course there was no greater calamity for a pianist. Schumann must be in torture. But at least she could play his compositions for him—

Without waiting for his consent, she went rapidly to the piano avoiding her father's questioning eyes.

"But it is much too difficult for you to play at sight," Schumann protested, coming up quickly behind her. It was she, he thought, who needed rescuing now.

Too difficult for Clara? Wieck gave Schumann an incredulous look and urged Clara to prove herself.

Dear Lord! Schumann thought, wouldn't it be better to play his composition himself and take the consequences rather than have Clara spoil it? His musician's pride revolted. Still, she had begun already. And Wieck looked prepared to enjoy a delicious triumph. Butterfly music—

The unhappy Schumann drew back. How clumsy Clara was with the beginning, how heavy-handed. He groaned inwardly. But one could not, after all, expect a mere child to understand the subtleties there, or to apply the proper coloring at once— he wanted to snap up the music from under her nose and race out of the room with it.

Soon, however, he was listening with more enthusiasm, for Clara, after her uncertain opening, had at last discovered the thread of the music and was giving it its proper line and tone.

Now! Now! he exulted. Astonishing child! She was proving not herself, but him!

He saw her smiling and wondered that so young a girl was capable of finding the secrets of his soul. But he mistook the meaning of Clara's smile. For her it had another source. As the music from the genius of Robert Schumann awoke to the sensitive understanding of her fingers, she was filled with unspeakable joy. For she knew what he did not yet fully comprehend. As a result of his unfortunate injury, it was *she* who would be his interpreter.

The bond more tightly woven between them this first day of May was now an unbreakable one. Surely it would go on forever—

I<small>T</small> <small>WAS NOT UNTIL</small> breakfast one morning of the following
week that Herr Wieck made his first acid comment on Schu-
mann's accident. Clara had just come into the dining room
and was about to begin her cereal when her father said to
Clementine, "I have here a letter I want to read to you."
He was waving a piece of scribbled paper in his fingers. "Sit
down, Clara. You may hear this too, if you like. It's quite
amusing."

"Perhaps you ought not to read it at the table, then,
Friedrich," Clementine said distractedly. "Clara, have your
fruit. . . ."

Frau Wieck's life in this talented household in which she
alone neither played a musical instrument nor was able to
sing, had unfortunately reduced itself to the most fanatic
dedication to domestic chores. There was a tragedy here
that met with no recognition from her husband, certainly not
from her stepdaughter, who had little patience with the
humorless pride Clementine bent on the strict supervision of
servants, the spotless appearance of her children, and the
scrubbed odor of her orderly run house. Indeed, an undercurrent of hostility often ran between these two, rising now and
again to open quarrels, for if Clara had a fault, it was her
refusal to see in the overanxious Clementine a person of
value, struggling to sublimate her disappointment at being

less in her husband's eye than Clara, less in her stepdaughter's than the faraway Marianne.

These just complaints resulted in curious turns of behavior on Clementine's part. She fluctuated between undue sternness at home, supercilious and hypocritical displays of affection for Clara and for Wieck's associates, and genuine emotions of love and pride for the ready-made family she had agreed to mother. Altogether, unfortunately, the effect was disturbing. Clara, at least, had come permanently to doubt her sincerity in anything.

But the true mark of Clementine's status in her home was clearly depicted now as, despite her objection, Wieck drew out his glasses, and to the delight of his curious children, proceeded to read the letter which so interested him. His tone as he read was purposefully colored with melodrama:

"Believe me, I am modest and have every reason to be so, but I am also brave, patient, confident and docile. I confide myself entirely in you. Take me as I am, but with forbearance. No blame shall depress me, no praise make me idle. A few pailfuls of very, very cold theory will not hurt me either, and I will not flinch under them. . . . Most honored sir, take my hand and lead me. I will follow wherever you go, and never take the bandage from my eyes lest they be dazzled by your presence. I wish you could read my heart now; all is very peaceful, with a soft morning breeze gently stirring. Trust in me—I will deserve to be called your pupil. . . ."

"I can't see anything amusing in it," Clementine said, as he concluded. Her eyes were unconsciously darting about the table to see if the white cloth were not already stained through the carelessness of Clara or one of her brothers. "To whom is it addressed, Friedrich?"

"To me, of course," he replied, maintaining a sly smile. "It is a letter Schumann addressed to me when I first agreed to take him on seriously as my pupil."

"I think it a beautiful letter, Father," Clara said. "I don't see why you should ridicule it."

"Well, perhaps that's your taste, Clara," he argued. "As for myself, I prefer things more plainly said. A little less poetry, a little more common sense. You must admit that Schumann's 'soft morning breeze' won't get him very far now."

"Are you blaming him, Father? He can't help what happened to his finger. He was only trying to improve himself, and to please you, too!"

"Clara! Lower your voice!" Clementine said. "It is not necessary to be so shrill."

Wieck laughed. "You must never scold the child for spirit, my dear. Allow it to her, even in behalf of Herr Schumann. It shows her to be a true artist."

Clementine unconsciously stiffened, but Wieck took no notice. "So!" he went on. "Schumann will be forced, after all, to confine himself to 'very, very cold theory,' as he calls it. Ironic, is it not? His mother must be trembling now for his future. Do you remember, Clementine, how he frightened her when he insisted on giving up law? 'He will never earn his bread by being a musician,' she said, and it was I who reassured her: 'Madame! I will undertake to develop your Robert into one of the greatest pianists now living'—bah!"

He folded the letter, clear disgust and disdain evidenced in his expression.

"How unjust you are, Father," Clara said in a trembling voice. "You yourself told me the other day you thought the *Papillons* excellent. You know Schumann will be a composer even if he never plays another note—"

The truth of the matter was that Wieck's admiration for Schumann's composition was even greater than Clara realized. He had, in fact, already determined to give the erring Schumann the help of having Clara play the piece in public at one of her future concerts. But he could not resist jabbing spurs of sarcasm into the young man's wound.

Nor did he fully understand his prejudice against Schumann. After all, it pleased his ego, did it not, to be so looked up to, to have his advice sought after in Schumann's fashion? Then, too, there was no denying the validity of Schumann's musical ideas—on the whole quite original. Yet, there was a disturbing quality—let Clara speak up for Schumann and he followed by speaking against him, and meant it, too. More often than not the young man rubbed him the wrong way— No, he did not altogether like Clara's Schumann—

Nevertheless, he allowed her now her point. "You are probably right," he said to her in a more conciliatory tone, replacing the letter in his pocket. "Schumann may yet turn out to be a composer. There *is* a spark of genius somewhere there— But we must wait first to see if he does not destroy it on some piece of foolishness the way he destroyed his hand. So! You can eat your breakfast now, Clara. No need to starve yourself on Schumann's account—!"

Summer days followed upon the May. In Connewitz woods families picnicked. There were baskets and red and white checked cloths on the grass, and children skipping across the streams. In the glassy water of the lake a pair of ducks glided with serenity while after them trooped the noisy ducklings dipping their bills and raising with their tails a rainbow shower.

Sitting at the lake's edge one afternoon the two Wieck boys, Alwin and Gustav, threw bits of bread into the water, and, their mama not being too close by, shouted with glee at the saucy antics of the birds.

"There's a green one. He's green all over," shouted Gustav.

"How do you know it's a *he*," asked Alwin disdainfully.

Gustav wrinkled his brow and threw a puzzled look at the duckling. "How do you know that it is not?" he demanded.

Alwin threw in his last crumb and folded his arms in a knowing manner. "I just know," he said proudly.

"But how?" persisted Gustav.

"It's a thing you either know or you don't," said Alwin with careless ease.

It was a dark moment for Gustav. He quickly lost interest in feeding the ducks and walked off in the direction of his parents, who sat under the trees enjoying a rest after their outdoor picnic.

"Have you used up the bread so soon?" asked his mother. "That's a pity, because there's nothing left now except cake."

"Oh, I don't want to feed them any more anyway," Gustav said crossly. He threw himself upon the grass beside Clara, his eyes black with misery.

"Oh, Gustav, don't tell me you and Alwin have been quarreling again," Clara said with a laugh.

"Even so, I don't think it very handsome to pout," Clementine said sternly to the sulking boy.

Wieck, enjoying one of those rare moments when dignity could be overlooked, was stretched out upon the grass, his eyes closed.

"Run along and make up with Alwin," he said, without raising his head. "What is it you two have been quarreling about anyway?"

"Nothing!" Gustav replied darkly between his teeth. He cast a jealous eye on his wiser brother who still stood by the pond, engaged now in talking to someone and that someone laughing uproariously. Gustav had not a doubt as to the source of their merriment.

Clara, sitting in a circle of pale blue skirt, her hat on her lap, followed his gaze.

"Why, there's Herr Schumann," she said. "Father, look! He's discovered Alwin. Mightn't we ask him over for cake?"

But Schumann seldom waited for invitations. He waved and walked quickly forward to join the little group under the trees. "Imagine it," he said, "I was just walking along, enjoying the sun when suddenly I looked up and saw Alwin standing by the lake. Good day, Herr Wieck."

"Hmnn. Yes. Good day, Schumann."

"Here is a piece of cake," said Clementine, handing him the last of her delicacy.

"You can't imagine," Schumann said between bites, "what an amusing conversation those two, Gustav and Alwin, have been having. They have been trying to decide . . ."

"We have not!" Gustav shouted, jumping up. He had turned red in the face.

"Why, Gustav! Shame on you!" Clara exclaimed in surprise.

"Apologize to Herr Schumann at once," his mother insisted.

"No, no, please. The boy is right. He's right, he's right," Schumann said in a soft tone, glancing compassionately down at the glowering culprit. "It is not my business to tell what has been transpiring between him and Alwin. It is I who apologize to you, Gustav." And he offered the boy his hand.

Gustav, disinclined to accept, lowered his head and twisted his toes into the ground. What a nuisance grown-up manners could be.

Sensitive to the boy's embarrassment, Schumann swiftly turned the conversation to other matters, engaging Wieck in a discussion of the state of musical affairs at the Gewandhaus.

In an amiable mood Wieck offered the young man a cigar, and between puffs, the two were soon heaping abuse on certain of Leipzig's "Philistines" who, in their opinion, were holding back the advancement of musical culture in Germany.

For Clara it was a pleasant sight to see the father she adored enjoying such good fellowship with her friend. She was miserable whenever they quarreled, and happy out of all bounds when they were like brothers. Now, as she helped Clementine clear up the picnic things, she kept half an ear on the animated conversation, enjoying the sound of Schumann's warm voice expressing discontent that Chopin's music was not yet being played enough by the popular artists. "But we will keep digging at them until they do!" she heard him cry out passionately.

Schumann, since his first published piece of criticism, the one in which he had expounded Chopin's genius, wanted very much to bring out a magazine of his own and often spoke of it. He now asked Wieck if Clara, at her forthcoming concert, was to play anything new—anything of special interest he might write about.

"Well," Wieck replied with a sly smile, "we will first give the audience what it is used to—all those sparkling virtuoso pieces, and then, when we have them satisfied, slip in one or two unfamiliar things—a little Chopin, a little— Well, perhaps another new composer whose name Clara will have on her program."

"Ah!" Schumann exclaimed, his face lighting with pleasure. "Do I know him?"

"As well as you know yourself."

Schumann threw Clara a look. Over the luncheon cloth, which she was helping Clementine to shake out, her smile and luminous eyes, if he guessed rightly, told him what he wanted to know.

Like an unrestrained schoolboy, he gave a shout of joy, and jumping up grabbed Clara's end of the bright cloth from her fingers, shaking it so vigorously that Clementine pleaded shrilly for him to compose himself.

"Come along, then, Clara!" he commanded, dropping the cloth as impulsively as he had taken it up. He took hold of her hand and pulled her along with him. "Walk with me awhile. If you have any good news to tell, begin for goodness sake, this moment. . . ."

As they went off together, hand in hand, Clementine's eyes followed after them. "I don't know if it is right any more for Clara to walk off with Schumann in that way. She is no longer a child, you know," she said suddenly to her husband.

"Clara? Not a child? Nonsense!" Wieck laughed good-naturedly, and began to puff vigorously on his cigar. But in this instance, Clementine was convinced that there were some things which she knew more about than her husband did. She would keep her silence for the present, but she would also keep her eyes open.

As soon as they were out of the hearing of her parents, Clara told Schumann what he wanted to know, that with her father's permission she was soon to perform his *Papillons*.

The summer world was all about them, its smells, its colors, its contentment. Here, midway between the restless excitement of spring, and the trembling, wondering pause of fall, here they walked, in the summertime of contentment, flooded with well-being, the young composer and his far younger interpreter.

"So! The old man thinks my composition not so bad after all," Schumann said, embracing with his eyes the whole of this summer world. He kicked at some pebbles underfoot, smiling inside as well as out. Today things were going fine for him. Today a bright angel sat upon his shoulder. There

were other times when this was not so, and he had, since
Clara's return, exhibited his varying moods so that she had
become solemnly aware of his more despondent days. Perhaps it was because she was growing up that she was first
noticing these times, when Schumann hardly spoke at all,
his handsome mouth pursed and silent, his eyes brooding
full and tortured. She walked beside him then, sharing his
mysterious troubles in the only way she could, taking to herself his puzzling unhappiness, and smiling again only when he
smiled.

Today's mood, however, took her fully in. Today he was
part child, part man. He suddenly began to run, urging her
on, in an attempt to overtake Alwin and Gustav whom he
saw in the distance. These two, friends again, had set off to
explore a thick little woods close by, where something more
than squirrels could be tracked down.

"Wait! Wait for me!" Clara laughed, breathlessly. Her
hair was flying, and the large hat she held in her hand was
trailing its two silken blue ribbons in the grass. Schumann
turned his head to laugh at her, and then gallantly slowed his
pace.

"What a slow one you are," he teased. "Now we've lost
your brothers. Well, never mind. Here's a pretty spot." He
threw himself down upon the grass beside the lake and Clara
gratefully slid down beside him.

"Look at the birds!" he said with a wave of his hand. "Look
at everything! Clara, are you as fond of the world as I am?"

It was his way of questioning, seldom expecting an answer.
She knew how to agree in silence. But then he put something
else to her.

"Tell me this, Clärchen. Do you see the two birds on the
lake? Do you see all their babes?"

"Yes," she said, puzzling at the light of amusement in his eyes.

"Now, tell me," he commanded, grinning. "Which one of the big birds would you say is the mama?"

Clara paused. Although she had been coming to Connewitz for many years, spending much of her time before this very lake, such a question had never even occurred to her. How much Schumann knew about everything, everything in the world. "She's the grayish one . . . I think," she said with a hesitant smile.

"And the ducklings?" Robert teased. "If Alwin were to tell you that *he* knows which are the males and which the females, what would you say to that?"

Fascinated by the sight of the playful babes dipping and preening in the sunlight, Clara studied them thoughtfully. She tilted her head to one side, unaware that she was blushing.

"I'm certain he doesn't know at all," she said after a moment. "Alwin is always boasting."

"Ah, but he looks at the world and asks questions!" Schumann replied. "He pokes about, digs up roots and asks, 'What is this?' Such a little man he is with such a busy head."

This statement was not meant as a reproach to his companion, but Clara felt its impact as a challenge to her own ignorance. So many hours spent over the piano—how had she time to go poking about, digging up roots? But such simple things as the names of flowers, how to tell one bird from the next . . . why she did not even know for sure. . . .

"*Are* they ducklings—the little ones, I mean?" She paused, frowning, very serious. "How do we know they are not baby geese? Oh, please! Herr Schumann! Don't tease." He had begun to roll over in the grass, overcome with laughter.

"You, you," he spluttered. "Can't tell the difference between a duck and a goose? . . . Oh, Clara. . . ." He turned about and pointed his finger at her. "You! *You* are a little duckling," he shouted in glee. "An innocent, a child. How precious you are. My delightful Clara! Promise me you will never grow up. Never, do you hear? How marvelous you are just as you are. . . ."

Humiliated, Clara suddenly grabbed up her hat, and started at a run in the direction of her parents. So! she thought, Alwin is to ask questions and be admired. But Clara, dear little Clara! She is to be laughed at and made fun of. And she must never grow up. Not ever! It was difficult to hold back her tears of rage. What did he think? That for him she would remain always a little girl and spend the rest of her life running to him for fairy tales?

Such were the thoughts in Clara's head as she ran blindly forward, finding cause for the first time to be angry at her adored Herr Schumann.

But he, as he sprang up after her, unaware that he was capable of causing the girl a moment's genuine pain, was repeating to himself in memory, and with affection, a description of Clara which he had read recently in an article in the *Cäcilia*, a music magazine published in Hamburg by his friend, Lyser. The article was said to have been written by none other than Heinrich Heine, who had seen Clara in Paris.

One might take Clara at first glance as she probably appears at home—for nothing more than an amiable little girl of thirteen, natural and childlike to her father and those about her. But to study her more closely would be to discern in her something very different. The fine, pretty little face with the strangely intent glance; the pleasant mouth with its suggestion of sentiment which now and then—particularly when she answers—becomes scornful or wistful; a compound of grace and carelessness in her movements, not studied, yet developed beyond her years. I freely confess it—these things excited in me a quite strange feeling which I cannot better describe than—"an echo of Clara's scornful-wistful smile." It is as if the child could tell a long tale woven of joys and grief—and yet—what does she know? Music.

Heine is right, Schumann thought. What does it matter how little else the girl knows? She is like all children, a creature to be studied, a mystery, "exciting in me quite a strange feeling." They are like shells, those little ones. One has only to listen closely to know the whole of the world. But what a strange thing that that innocent little girl, that babe who does not know a duck from a goose, should know the greatest secret of all.

He caught up with her and his laughter was the joy of true recognition. *I have kinship with her,* he shouted inwardly, *Clara and I . . . we know music.*

PART TWO

AWAKENING

NINE

In the spring of 1834 Ernestine von Fricken arrived in Leipzig. She came on a wet, misty April morning when the whole of the town smelled of smoke and soaked leaves and pedestrians picked their way along the muddy streets under great black umbrellas. To the Wiecks, whose house guest she was to be, Ernestine presented a picture of happy contrast, a bright, graceful girl of seventeen with the charming habit of flinging back her yellow hair whenever she laughed. Unlike the temperamental April, she seemed a warm and open personality with no deep currents to be explored, no somber moods to be endured. Her complexion, her richly curved mouth, her well-shaped, ample figure all bore the stamp of healthy living. She was, apparently, as fresh and uncomplicated as a farm girl whose simple beauty is synonymous with the happiness of seventeen.

As she stepped lightly from her cab that first morning, running with a burst of laughter through the rain to reach their door, no one suspected, and least of all Clara, that such a cheerful girl could bring, as April sometimes brings, the sorrows of first loss, the tears and pain that come with sudden change. In fact, for Clara, whose need of a companion was great, Ernestine was the promise of a sister.

The two girls had met in Plauen, one of those meetings, seemingly formal and momentary, destined to change the lives of both. Clara had journeyed there to give a concert, and in her audience on that evening was Baron von Fricken, an amateur musician who had come from his home town of Asch to hear her play. Beside him sat the radiant Ernestine, whose musical education he himself had already begun; but as he listened to Clara's brilliant performance, the baron could not help wondering what would happen if Ernestine too had the advantage of being trained by Leipzig's Friedrich Wieck. He did not ponder the question too long, for by the time the concert was concluded he had already made up his mind. Wieck, upon hearing his proposition, was overjoyed. It was certainly a feather in his cap to have the musical baron's daughter come to him as a pupil.

The two girls, meanwhile, having exchanged greetings, stood silently by, waiting for their parents to conclude whatever business they were about. It was not until later, when Clara was returning to Leipzig, that she learned from her father what had transpired. She, too, but for reasons far removed from her father's, was overjoyed. Almost at first glance she had recognized in Ernestine many fine points of young womanhood to which she secretly aspired. How grown-up the girl seemed compared with herself. What mysteries of life must she already know! The tilt of that pretty head, the half-teasing smile of her eyes as she glanced about the room, the grace of those white, plump fingers as they picked up a lace glove carelessly dropped! Clara, from the corner of her eye, watched with curious, worshipful envy.

What was it like, she wondered, to be an Ernestine, to live quietly in a little town across the Bohemian border, to be surrounded and pursued by many beaux? That the girl had admirers was plain to see. One only had to look at her.

All at once Clara despised her own dainty, childish gown, the ribbon which held up her high curls, the little-girl slippers which showed from under her skirt. She looked with chagrin at her nails, kept trimmed close so as not to interfere with the keys, and thought her fingers quite unattractive. No wonder the baron's daughter barely gave her a glance. But upon looking up again, she met a pair of friendly, smiling eyes quite without scorn or challenge. Nothing was harbored there save a warm glow of contentment, radiating lights which invited friendship. How happy the girl must be!

Clara gave an inward little sigh. It was not the first time she had felt this kind of envy. Especially during the past year had she begun to grow weary of her *Wunderkind* role, of always walking within the shelter of her father's careful affection. Neither he nor her family's circle of friends seemed to understand at all that their "amazing" child was growing, developing into a girl seeking to emerge from her nest of silk, and eager, if only for a few dangerous moments, to fly close to the sun like the daring Icarus. By hundreds of invisible, loving strands they were holding her back to a warm cocoon of safety. Where, in such a world, was she to find the experiences needed for womanhood?

No wonder, then, that she leaned upon the image of her new friend for something far richer than prestige or casual companionship. The bright-spirited Ernestine, who could accept with natural ease and charm Clementine's too obvious, doting mannerisms, who could obey Wieck's sternest commands at the piano with agreeable smiles, she it was who would play for Clara a role that neither Clementine nor Nanny had ever been able successfully to fill. She, with her touch of perfume, her jeweled clasps caught in the nest of hair at the back of her head, her hand mirror modestly studied for all the right facial tones, *she* would pull away at those threads of childhood and point the way—out there!

"But I don't *need* a room all to myself," Ernestine insisted to Clementine that first day. "I thought Clara and I would be together. We can be, can't we, Clara? You wouldn't mind?"

Clementine looked regretfully at the spotless room she had meant to be Ernestine's. Days of preparation had gone into sewing the soft white curtains, hemming the dainty skirt that covered the dressing table legs, polishing the two Dresden figurines which stood on the mantel. But Clara, who had accused her stepmother of behaving as if royalty itself were expected, was secretly delighted that Ernestine was turning it all down. Didn't it serve Clementine right for playing the grand lady?

Arm in arm the two girls escaped to the peculiar delights of the crowded little room they chose to share, while Clementine, with a quivering smile of defeat, quietly closed the door on her precious work of art.

The days that followed proved happy ones for Clara. She and Ernestine were up at dawn each morning, for her father insisted upon industriousness, especially for his new pupil who had yet so much to learn at the piano. But as soon as they had free time, the two girls locked themselves away in their room to talk. Ernestine reminisced almost tirelessly of her romantic adventures in Asch, all of them harmless enough, but thrilling to Clara, who only wished she had similar ones to report. She could, however, boast of her friendship with Robert Schumann, who gave her in manuscript form his new compositions to try out; she, too, she told Ernestine, was now studying composition and often gave him suggestions for themes.

One afternoon she handed Ernestine a little magazine, recently published, titled *Neue Leipziger Zeitschrift für Musik*. "It's Schumann's own!" she exclaimed excitedly. "He's brought it out himself. Isn't it wonderful?"

"But *everything* your Schumann does is wonderful," Ernestine teased her. "You should hear yourself, Clara. The way you talk about him!"

Without bothering to give a serious glance at it, she returned the magazine to Clara, and lay back against the huge white pillows, already thinking of other things. Clara was dismayed at her indifference, and refused to allow the subject to die so easily. "You should know what effort Schumann put into this first issue," she went on aggressively. "It will soon have everyone in Leipzig talking. Do you realize, Ernestine, what it means to have such a journal, one dedicated entirely to music? Why, to hold it is like holding Schumann's heart in your hands!"

Ernestine gave her a fleeting, condescending smile.

"But it's true," Clara insisted. "Ask Father, ask anyone who knows him. They'll all say the same."

"Will they?"

"You won't even question it when you get to know him. You'll feel then the same as I do. I've always liked him the best of all our acquaintances."

"Obviously!"

"You're laughing at me, Ernestine. Don't you believe anything I say?" Clara was now behaving with petulance, for still uncertain of herself in their relationship, she sometimes unfairly questioned the older girl's sincerity. "No wonder I care for Schumann so much," she pouted. "He has me for a friend regardless of the difference in our age. And he never shows me scorn, or makes me feel in the least afraid of him."

"Afraid of him!" Ernestine exclaimed indignantly. "Well, I should hope not, Clara. After all, *you're* the celebrity. Everyone in Germany knows Clara Wieck. As for Robert Schumann, who has heard of him?"

"Perhaps not many," Clara soberly replied. "But one day that will all be changed, and *he* will be far more famous than

I. Did it ever occur to you, Ernestine, that after I die no one will be able to remember how well I played? But Schumann's compositions can be performed forever."

She was so solemn that Ernestine burst into open laughter. "Indeed?" she asked with twinkling eyes. "I must say that this—this genius of yours is fortunate to have such a faithful friend as you. But seriously, Clara, for your own sake, never put men on pedestals."

Clara reflected on this bit of wisdom, then shook her head. "One just can't help it with Schumann. Even you, Ernestine, when you meet him, will be doing the same."

"Pooh!" replied Ernestine instantly, with a toss of her head. "I tell you what, Clara. When he comes, your Schumann, I shan't even bother to look at him. No! Not even for you! And I'm sure I don't care whether or not he bothers to look at me, for I have far too many admirers in Asch already!"

TEN

Musikparten or "at homes with music" were as much in vogue in Leipzig as in Paris. Professional as well as amateur musicians liked nothing better than to gather together in some fashionable drawing room to enjoy to their heart's content much of the fine music seldom played in concert halls. But whereas in Paris, as Wieck had observed, the first requirement of success was to be recognized by the nobility, an artist having to be as much a master of the social graces as of his own art, there was in Leipzig a stubborn musical tradition which would not die aborning even if princes chose to turn their backs upon it. For a new class, the growing, powerful bourgeoisie, was already beginning to take over where feudal barons and princes left off, and willingly opened its doors to music lovers.

Karl Voigt, one of the wealthiest of Leipzig merchants, was renowned not only for his endowment of performances of Beethoven's *Ninth Symphony* at the Gewandhaus, but for the many memorable *Musikparten* he sponsored. Both he and his musical wife, Henriette, offered their hospitality generously to successful as well as striving musicians, and they were seldom refused, except perhaps by the proud Friedrich Wieck, who chose to run rival parties of his own. But Wieck made no protest if his friends or pupils chose to attend without him. Schumann was one of those who went often to the Voigts'. It was not unusual to see him, long past the midnight hour, leaving the Voigt house with his friend and roommate,

Ludwig Schunke, both of them heading for the *Kaffebaum* for one last round of talk before retiring. Rumor had it that Schumann was madly in love with Henriette, but most of his intimate friends who understood him well knew that he believed in establishing strong friendships with women as well as men, and they refused to give credence to this piece of gossip. Wieck, however, was one who chose to believe what he heard. A similar rumor had once persisted, connecting the impulsive Schumann with Agnes Carus, the doctor's wife, and Schumann himself admitted to learning Schubert *Lieder* from her lips. Since Wieck had displayed on that occasion an amused skepticism of the platonic nature of the young man's affair, upon learning of this new attachment to Henriette, he began with sly smiles to refer to his former pupil as a "man of the world."

Toward the middle of May, an invitation arrived for Ernestine to attend one of the Voigt evening parties. Wieck at first refused, for he did not wish her to go without him, nor was he willing to alter his usual custom of remaining aloof. But, rather to his own surprise, he found himself weakening under the charm of the girl's petulant pleas, and could not bring himself to withdraw his half-hearted consent once she had raised herself on tiptoe to plant an impulsive kiss on his stubborn, high-boned cheek. He gave in. Yes, she could go to the Voigts', but only if their carriage called for her. He himself was much too busy to give up an evening to play the escort.

For two hours before the time set for the arrival of Henriette's carriage, Clementine, as busy as a mother hen, hung dotingly over her young charge, supervising every detail of her dress. And Clara looked on with genuine delight as her stepmother's deft fingers braided her friend's soft hair and set it into place with a small, sparkling comb. Once this operation was concluded, Ernestine drew on her rose silk gown and swung herself about on her little heels in front of the mirror. Clara thought her very beautiful.

"They will love you! They will all love you!" she said proudly, as soon as Clementine had left them alone in the room.

"Will they?" Ernestine pressed Clara's hand in happiness. "How nice it would be, Clara, if you too were going. . . ."

Clara's smile in return was rueful. "They have me there now and again, but on special occasions when I perform. I don't suppose they think me grown-up enough yet for dancing."

"Nonsense! I went to my first dance when I was barely thirteen. Only speak up, Clara! Assert yourself more. And don't, for heaven's sake, be so solemn all the time. Laugh! Be gay! Everyone will take more notice of you then."

"Ernestine! Come!" Clementine's shrill voice carried up from below. "The carriage is waiting. . . ."

"Good-by, dear Clara. Give me a kiss and wish me luck."

As she descended the stairway, Ernestine caught sight of Alwin and Gustav, who, in their nightclothes, were hiding behind the banister. "Goodnight, you little scamps," she whispered, blowing them a kiss. The two boys, quite unconscious of why her smile should cause them to suffer, blushed in the darkness. Both were half in love with her already.

Clara, meanwhile, stood at her window, watching Ernestine being helped into the carriage, and remained to listen until the sound of the departing vehicle had died away. The night was calm. Across the square, under the street lamp, a man and woman could be seen walking arm in arm. They paused for a moment to look up into one another's eyes, and then, with lowered heads, walked on once more, slowly, into the darkness. Now all was still, the street entirely deserted. This

sudden, profound quiet had a strange effect upon her. Quite
unexpectedly she felt as if she were going to cry.

"How foolish of me," she murmured aloud, after a moment.
"What is it, anyway, I am crying about?" And to shake off
this mysterious mood, she rushed from the room.

In the hall she discovered her brothers still at the banister.
"Go to bed, now. Quickly," she said in a voice quite unlike
her own.

"Read us a story then, Clara," Gustav demanded in a
bargaining way.

"No, no! Do as I say," she commanded irritably. She did
not, however, wait to see if they obeyed. She continued her
journey downstairs where she found her parents in the drawing
room, both in silent occupations, her father with his usual
stock of papers, her stepmother at her crocheting.

"Well, Clara, I thought you were already preparing for
bed," Clementine said as she came into the room.

What an annoyance. Here was Ernestine just off to a party
and her stepmother could think of nothing better for her
than bed. "It's too early to go to bed," she replied, barely able
to conceal her crossness.

Wieck looked up to consult the clock. "Not too early
tonight, I think, Clara," he said, observing thoughtfully her
eyes which still showed signs of emotion. "So! There's been
plenty of excitement for you tonight, eh, *Liebchen*, what
with sending Ernestine off to her party? That girl manages
to get everything off balance. Take care she doesn't upset
your schedule. Go to bed! It's good advice. I will be going
up myself, soon."

He could not have chosen a more unfortunate time to
support Clementine, for Clara saw him now in league with
her stepmother and turned her back on him, feeling keenly
that he had betrayed her. "Speak up! Assert yourself." That

was what Ernestine had advised. Well, tonight was one time she would not walk up the stairs like a mechanical doll at their bidding. She was not a child any more. They must understand *that*.

Deliberately she walked over to the far end of the room, intending to sit at the piano, but as if some power beyond her own was pulling her along, she did not stop there but at the open window instead.

There it was again, that mysterious world of night! The moon appeared, brightening the garden. *Come, Clara*, it seemed to be saying, *what are you doing in that stuffy room? Come and fill your lungs with the scent of night roses.* She leaned her head pensively against the casing. How dull and unsatisfying everything at home seemed tonight. A strange longing, the same as had come over her upstairs, rose sharply in her chest. So heavy was her oppression that a sigh, loud enough to be heard at the other end of the room, escaped her.

"Look at Clara!" Clementine whispered to Wieck.

"Eh?"

"Watch her—by the window. I know that look. She will be wanting to go to parties herself soon."

"What are you saying? Clara's not light-headed like the other one. She has more important things to think about."

Clementine laughed softly. "Has she? Well, maybe. But did you hear her sigh? A touch of spring, I imagine, affects her like any other."

Clara, who had heard every word, stiffened in anger. Why didn't Clementine attend to her own affairs? What did she know of how others were feeling?

"Come! Do as I say and kiss me goodnight, Clara," Wieck suddenly called out. Clara stood motionless for a moment as if strengthening her will for disobedience, but as she now

preferred escape to remaining in the same room with her
stepmother, she decided to come forward. "Good night,
Father. . . ."

"But have you no kiss for your mother?" Clementine called
after her as she was about to leave the room.

Clara turned about, but with such obvious reluctance that
Clementine was prompted to remark to her husband, "Notice,
Friedrich, one has to be grateful for favors. . . ."

It was already past eleven when Clara finally heard the
Voigt carriage draw up before the house. A murmur of voices
and laughter sounded from below her window. She quickly
lit her candle, expecting that Ernestine would come up at
any moment, but it was fully half an hour before her friend
made her appearance. Ernestine's cheeks were flushed the
way they might have been had she come out of the snow
rather than spring moonlight, and her hair was softly loosened
as she had already begun to pull out the pins on her way up
the stairs.

She turned herself about dreamily, both arms crossed over
her chest as she smiled at Clara. "I'm glad you waited up. I
had a wonderful time . . . a wonderful time," she repeated
softly. She seemed to Clara like a dancer who, once having
known the music which had set her into motion, could never
again be still.

Clara laughed, almost forgetting now what torture it had
been to lie awake waiting for her. "Only stop dancing now,
Ernestine," she pleaded, "and tell me everything that happened, every detail."

Ernestine tossed her cape carelessly onto the chair and sank
down before the mirror, staring into it with the joy of her
memories still reflected in her eyes. "How can I tell you

everything? Tonight my whole life changed—it was like a miracle. I don't know how to tell you."

"But you must. I've been waiting patiently all these hours," Clara begged.

Ernestine turned about and leaned forward slightly, too pre-occupied with her own thoughts to notice how intense Clara was as she sat against the great down pillows, hugging her knees. She began to unfasten her gown, smiling one moment, closing her eyes as if in ecstasy the next, while Clara, her black hair cascading to her shoulders, watched her every motion with mounting impatience. Finally she spoke, saying in a provoca-tive way, "Listen, Clara, but you must promise not to repeat a word I tell you. Tonight I met him—your Schumann I mean."

"Now!" Clara interrupted with happy satisfaction. "Now you know him."

Ernestine took up her brush, cupped a handful of hair in her palm and began to smooth out the wavy strands with the stiff bristles. "You put it too strongly. It isn't always easy to *know* a person just at first meeting, but we had a talk after he brought me home."

"Oh, then it was *his* voice I heard downstairs."

"Yes. He brought me to the door, but he wouldn't say good night right off. You should have made it clearer to me about him, Clara. How he looks when he says certain things, how his eyes smile, how kind his voice can be when it takes on that intimate tone. He gets me to confessing all sorts of foolish things. 'Yes,' I was saying to myself all the while, 'I think I can love this Schumann!' "

"There! You see?" Clara cried out. "Didn't I say so? It is impossible not to."

Releasing her brush, Ernestine quickly tied up her hair and slipped into bed. She folded her arms beneath her head, gazing

at the ceiling. "I *am* glad you waited up, Clara. It would
have been dreadful to come home to a dark room with no one
to talk to, especially when there is so much . . . so much
bursting inside me. Let me tell you everything, just as it
happened. Yes, blow out the candle now, if you want. I'm
so happy. Listen. He was standing across the room when
I arrived at the Voigts' and Henriette took me by the arm
and said, 'I'm certain you must have met Schumann already,
he is so often at the Wiecks'.' I shook my head and laughed.
Suddenly it seemed so obvious to me that everyone was
plotting to bring us together. 'No,' I told her, 'I have *not*
met Schumann, nor do I wish to. Despite all Clara says, I'm
sure he's just an ordinary man.' She gave me a curious look,
but didn't insist. What a wonderful hostess! All evening the
young men were around her. She has a way of laughing, a
warm friendly way. Schumann, I noticed, never left her side.
Others danced, but he looked on, his mouth all puckered up
as if he were whistling. I thought him quite amusing. Later
Henriette urged him to play one of his compositions. I was
certain he would refuse, considering what you told me about
his lame hand, but he went right away to the piano and began. Naturally, I was curious. Henriette came to stand beside me, and halfway through she whispered, 'Now do you
think him ordinary?' I shrugged, but I think she knew I was
impressed. What a fascinating face he has! Afterward, of
course, I allowed myself to be taken to him—and we danced."

She broke off, her silence revealing more closely than words
the depth of her feeling. Clara, to whom the realization had
come slowly, understood at last that she and Ernestine had
been speaking of love with different meanings. Curiously, she
was no longer glad.

"So he brought you home," she said in a strained tone.
"And what did you talk about?"

"Everything. Music, people, the moon. How many questions he asks! All kinds of personal things. He drained me dry. For a musician he makes quite an impression, your Schumann. I'm sure a girl would not be ashamed if . . . she married him."

"Marry him!" Clara laughed, despite herself. "Are you thinking of that already? But Schumann will never marry."

Ernestine was shocked at her positive tone and told her so. "What a strange thing to say, Clara."

Clara's face burned in the darkness. Ernestine was right. It was indeed an impulsive statement. Whatever had made her say it? Yet she felt a strong need to defend herself. "It's just that composers don't marry so easily," she argued. "They haven't the time. Yes, that's it."

Ernestine turned away, her gesture of disbelief visible even in the darkened room. And Clara made no effort to hold her any longer, for she was busy now recalling an almost forgotten incident.

Shortly after her return from Paris, she had gone on a brief concert tour, performing first at Schumann's town of Zwickau. A portion of his first symphony was to have its premier performance there on the same evening, and they were both immensely pleased because it was the first time that their names would appear together on the same program. He, of course, had come along for the momentous occasion, and insisted that she and her father be guests at his home. It was then, for the first time, that she met his mother. Frau Schumann, although she was aging, was still a beautiful woman, but what one noticed first about her was the sad quality of her features, especially a certain melancholy look about the eyes. It was as if she were brooding over some secret sorrow. Robert seemed constantly to be trying to woo her out of her mysterious troubles with one of his little jokes, but to no avail.

On the evening of the concert, he left early with her father to inspect the condition of the piano in the hall. She was to remain at his home until almost time for the performance to begin, when he would call for her. For a long while after his departure, Frau Schumann remained sitting at the window, unsmiling, uncommunicative. But suddenly she made a motion, inviting Clara to her side and pointing to the fields below.

"There," she said in a low voice, "are the fields where my Robert used to play as a boy. How happy and bright he was then. He showed such promise and his father, his dear father, was so proud!" Her voice broke and she sighed before continuing. "My dear child Emilie—I suppose Robert has told you about his sister who died at nineteen—*she* was alive then. Those were the happy days."

An uncomfortable silence followed. The ticking of the clock became extraordinarily loud. For a while longer the old lady continued to gaze out of the window in her melancholy way, but suddenly her face brightened with a strange intensity.

"Look!" she cried. "My son is coming!" She stood up, reaching for Clara's arm, as if her joy were too great to be experienced without support. After a moment, she fixed her remarkable eyes upon Clara's own and said with an odd but tender emphasis, "*Someday you must marry my Robert.*"

Those fantastic words, barely comprehensible then, no longer, in retrospect, seemed incredible to Clara. They burned now with genuine meaning in her mind. As gradually she drifted off to sleep, a wonderful dream unfolded itself to her with the magic of a night-blooming flower. She was smiling now.

ELEVEN

UNTIL HIS MEETING with Ernestine von Fricken, Robert Schumann had given little thought to entertaining girls. In Zwickau, as a youth, he had had a momentary infatuation with a certain Liddy but had soon given her up, due to her deficiency of intellect. Later on, in Leipzig, where he had come to study law, he preferred the exciting, intellectual world of his comrades at the university, spending his evenings in a haze of cigar smoke and a turmoil of stimulating argument. He was an avid reader of poetry, a student of philosophy, and above all, a dedicated musician, taking these much more to his heart than the law, which he soon grew to detest. For him the romanticism of literature and the lure of musical fame had such a glow that neither his mother's tearful protests nor the sober warnings of Herr Rudel, his guardian since his father's death, could settle him down to his studies, even after he had left Leipzig for the more carefree atmosphere of Heidelberg University.

At Easter, in the year 1830, when he was twenty years old, he made a journey with his best friend Töpken to hear Paganini, and afterward could not rest. The incredibility of himself as a man of business—a man of law—finally made him spring from his bed at five o'clock one July morning and sit down before his open window to state his case to his mother:

Good morning, Mama, [he wrote] . . . my whole life has been a twenty years' war between poetry and prose, or let us say, music and law. . . . Now I stand at the parting of the roads and shudder at the question: whither? If I follow my own bent, it points, and as I believe, correctly, to music. . . . We always called it an uncertain future and a precarious livelihood. . . .

To the practical Rudel he wrote, "I was born for music. . . ." His mother yielded and put his case to Wieck as objectively as she could: "All rests on your decision, the peace of a loving mother, the whole happiness for life of a young and inexperienced man who lives but in a higher sphere and will have nothing to do with practical life. . . ."

Victorious, Schumann returned to Leipzig in the custody of Wieck to begin at last his journey on that "higher sphere." Since then he had hardly put his head out of it long enough to seek the normal pleasure of a girl's companionship. When he was not at home composing, or with his friends, the musicians Julius Knorr and Ludwig Schunke, with whom he sometimes enjoyed a game of bowling or ice skating in winter, he enjoyed best long solitary walks seeking the peace and inspiration his cherished pastoral countryside of Zwickau had given him. Occasionally he would take a child along, and think, as he watched its uninhibited joy at each new scent and sound, of what Jean Paul Richter, the novelist, had written: "Children, you are nearest to God: the smallest plant is the one nearest the sun."

For Schumann, with his dreams, it was a good, a healthy life. He cherished and was cherished in return by his family. The modest inheritance he had from his father, along with generous gifts now and then from his indulgent mother, permitted him the few luxuries he required—a decent suit, his cigars, an occasional beer, and of course, the Gewandhaus concerts. Except to be rid of sporadic bouts of depression which had become intensified since the death of his brother, Julius, followed shortly after by the loss of his favorite sister-in-law, Rosalie, he asked for nothing more, only to continue on in this way until he had achieved his greatest dream—recognition as a composer. It was not that he was averse to the pleasures of love: he simply had not made room in his life for them.

Then one May evening, he saw Ernestine von Fricken. He heard the softness of her voice, the challenge of her laughter. In late moonlight, he helped her down from Henriette's carriage and escorted her to the Wieck doorstep, disturbingly alert to trivial details—her rose-colored gown, her comb glistening in the honey-toned hair, her unblemished complexion to which she added nothing more than the bloom of health. These were enough to make him give a spring over the hedge after he parted from her, and go whistling home in the dark.

He soon began to make an appearance at the Wiecks' every afternoon. How well he knew the routines. After dinner, weather permitting, the two girls, along with Clara's brothers, always went for their afternoon walk. "Be sure to call me as soon as Schumann comes," Ernestine would caution Clara, and run up the stairs to recomb her hair. Later, with Alwin and Gustav taking the lead, the three would set out for their excursion. It was seldom that they explored the stalls or the markets, for Schumann's nose always quivered in the direction of the distant fields. He never wearied of seeking out bird coveys or of sitting on the banks of the River Pliesse after a rain. The moment the noises of the busy thoroughfare were behind them, he became like a freed prisoner, his voice taking on the ring of sweet release, his arms waving and gesticulating as he talked, his face brightening with every step closer to nature.

But, for Clara, these walks were no longer the same as in

days of old. Schumann talked almost exclusively to Ernestine, while she, receiving none of his attention, walked moodily a step or two behind. Schumann, who in the past was given to long silences, talked a great deal now, expounding at length for Ernestine his philosophy of music and art, and quoting lavishly from his favorite books and poems. Once, when Clara bravely put in a word of her own to reveal to him that she had now made time to read some of his favorite authors, he threw her an astonished look and said, with a grin, "Oh, is it you, little Clara? I had almost forgotten you were here." For Clara that was a bitter pill to swallow.

She began to take jealous pleasure in observing Ernestine's failings, and wondered how long it would take Schumann to discover that his enchanted girl, with her smiling silences, was only trying to hide from him her ignorance of such names as Jean Paul Richter, Heine, Goethe, Eichendorff. Ernestine had never even heard of them. Clara could barely refrain from indulging in one of those wistful-scornful smiles, but her jealousy of her friend certainly added nothing to her happiness.

One afternoon, in an unusually exuberant mood, Schumann caught hold of Ernestine's hand and began to recite from Heine:

> Over me a melody
> Softly steals; oh, ring!
> Ring out, sing out far and free!
> Little song of Spring.

> Ring out till you reach the place
> Where the flowers grow.
> Should a rose turn up her face,
> Say I said Hello!

Ernestine did not know what to make of him as he lifted his head toward the wide heavens, communicating, as it were, with the universe. She secretly thought him somewhat mad, but it pleased her all the same, because, thinking the poem his own, she saw herself as his inspiration.

"What a lovely poem," she said quite sincerely. "You should take up being a poet, Robert, instead of a musician."

Clara caught her breath. Now was the moment when Schumann would surely open his eyes, take in Ernestine's limitations, and see with whom he was so foolishly infatuated. But his laughter, when it came, was not ridicule—no, nothing like it.

"Poet—musician—we are the same!" he exclaimed happily. "Do you recall, Ernestine, how Eichendorff put it? 'In nature as well as in the labyrinth of the human heart sleeps from the beginning of time a wonderful and eternal song given to the poet to deliver.' Jean Paul said it another way. 'Sound shines like the dawn and the sun rises in the form of sound. . . .' There you have it, Ernestine. Music and poetry! Both the voice of nature, and in nature, the seed of song."

Ernestine stared at him, nodding mutely. Nothing of what he had said penetrated her pretty head. But he was oblivious.

"Listen," he said, drawing her forward across the path to where Alwin and Gustav had settled themselves knee-deep in a field of flowers. "I shall tell you, dear Ernestine, how it is with *this* poet. In my head are hundreds and hundreds of flowers, wild, unweeded, beautiful! Whenever I have the fancy, I pluck one, and lo—it turns into a melody. Then, in its place, another grows. You see how fortunate I am? One eternal springtime—"

On another afternoon, he took both girls rowing on the lake at the Rosenthal. Ernestine had a pale blue scarf wound

about her throat, and her hair fell in soft wisps across her face
as she leaned to the side, trailing her fingers in the water.
Clara sat beside her, holding her sun hat on her lap, trying
to avoid watching Schumann's expression of adoration as he
looked at Ernestine. He, in his happy fashion, kept up a constant stream of chatter for Ernestine's benefit, who made no
response at all other than to glance up at him now and then
with an entrancing smile.

A pair of swans went proudly by, ignoring loud cries of
praise issuing from a nearby boat in which sat a gaudily dressed
middle-aged woman who, Clara thought, must be an actress,
judging from the amount of paint on her hollow cheeks. Her
companion, a young man barely out of his teens, outdid himself with rowing to keep up with the beautiful birds. "Oh,
catch them, catch them," the lady cried out. "Make them
come to me!"

Clara thought her ridiculous. In his haste, the young man
brought his boat dangerously close to theirs, Schumann managing to avoid collision only because of Clara's warning cry.
He, too, now seemed ridiculous to her. Was he not, for the
sake of Ernestine's pretty face, making the same sort of
spectacle of himself as the lady gushing over the swans?

For a moment she doubted herself. Perhaps, after all, he
was not what she had thought him in the past. Perhaps she
had been worshipping a false god. His eyes! At this moment
they were no different from that silly young man's, the one
who went wildly chasing after swans.

So! She closed her eyes, thankful that her burden was gone.
Now she need care about him no longer. No more pain. No
more anguish. She was free!

"Look at Clara! Lazy one! Sleeping on such a beautiful
afternoon." A sudden splash of water hit against her face

and she opened her eyes to see him laughing at her. Ernestine, too. Oh, it was easy for *them* to be happy.

But she saw that Schumann was looking at her in his old, tender way as he said, "Wake up, Clärchen, Chiarina . . . this is no time for sleeping."

Clärchen. Chiarina. These the names he called her. Yes, he loved her still, after his own fashion, and she must go on loving him.

It simply could not be helped.

TWELVE

Wieck was in a rare, affable mood. With the approach of summer, marking the end of his busy season, he began to relax, noting with amusement the atmosphere of romance which had entered his household. It did not take Clementine this time to point out to him how the wind blew. He saw for himself all the little signs of love—Schumann and Ernestine were both wearing their hearts on their sleeves. Wieck thought the girl a good catch for Schumann, providing the young man could arrange it with the baron. As von Fricken's son-in-law, he could pursue his musical career without fear of financial stress, the more so since the baron, an amateur musician himself, would probably not be averse to sponsoring Schumann's ambitions. Toward Ernestine, who could not bring herself to concentrate any longer on the complexities of scales and theory, running as she did restlessly from the piano every little while to see if Schumann was coming up the walk, Wieck became helpfully tolerant. It was a new role for him, this playing Cupid. He thought it would be exceptionally clever on Schumann's part if a match could be sponsored, and he was always in favor of these "clever" arrangements.

He had other reasons for his cheerful mood. Clementine was expecting a baby. It pleased him to see her with her expression of almost smug contentedness as she sat at her knitting, surveying the comings and goings of the young people. Although he did not make a spectacle of his pride, he too was looking forward to the arrival of the new child. It was coming at a good time.

The last year had proved successful on many accounts. By now, Clara's reputation was soundly established in Germany, and her concerts were enriching not only his artistic pride but the family till as well. There was no longer any question as to his skill in teaching or in management. Friedrich Wieck's finger was in every musical pie in Leipzig. Especially did it please his ego to play fatherly adviser, as it were, to the younger generation of musicians who had recently begun publicly to show their respect for his opinions in the *Neue Leipziger Zeitscrift für Musik*. As Schumann's part in this promotion was not unknown to him, he felt at this moment a jovial, reciprocal interest in the younger man, displaying toward him at times almost too familiar a camaraderie.

He took it upon himself after a brief period of observation to communicate to Baron von Fricken the state of affairs between Schumann and Ernestine, so as to pave the way for Schumann's inevitable proposal for the girl's hand and to hint at the same time at the logical reason for Ernestine's diminishing interest in her own musical efforts. Schumann, meanwhile, still reeling from his first genuine experience in love, was writing of Ernestine to his mother:

She has a wonderfully pure, childlike nature, is gentle and thoughtful, has a deep affection for me and for everything artistic, and she is unusually musical—in short, just the one I might wish for a wife; and, I will whisper this in your ear, my good mother, if the future were to ask me whom I should choose, I would answer with decision, this one. . . .

Clara tried bravely enough to hide her feelings, but each day that passed became more painful. Ernestine was growing more and more secretive. She no longer seemed the warm, open-hearted friend she had been before. A rather curious relationship had developed between her and Henriette Voigt, the older woman coming for her in her carriage and carrying her off, sometimes for an entire afternoon. It soon became obvious that on those same afternoons Schumann did not make his usual appearance, and Clara concluded rightfully enough that Henriette too was encouraging the romance, acting with Wieck's approval as chaperone for the two.

Wieck at first did not notice the change in Clara. Indeed it was only her two brothers, feeling the brunt of her varying moods, who took to speculating. When they accompanied her on afternoon excursions they were surprised how quickly she could veer from sullen behavior to overcharged gaiety. On one occasion she startled Alwin by declaring crossly, "Oh, I don't care what we do today or any other day. I wouldn't care if we stayed out on the lake all afternoon and never went home."

She was, they noticed, less energetic than usual, complaining often of headaches and attributing the malady to the oppressive Leipzig summer.

"I wish I could go away," she said to them one afternoon. "I wonder if it is any cooler in Dresden."

At home she stayed as much as possible out of Clementine's path, preferring on rainy afternoons to read or help Nanny with her chores. Occasionally she would drive herself so hard at practicing that her father intervened, saying she was tiring herself needlessly. But one day, when she was taken with this compulsion, he left off his own work and asked her if she would not like to have a go at some four-hand music.

"If you like, Father," she replied carelessly. "What shall we play?"

"Let's do the Paganini. To think, Clara, you were such a

little girl that other time! And Paganini could hardly believe his ears. All in all, we have had great fun, haven't we?"

"Yes, Father, we have."

He brought out the music, and settled himself beside her at the piano. He was extraordinarily relaxed and smiling. They were alone in the house as Clementine was visiting her friend, Frau Vogel, and had taken the two boys along with her. Earlier in the day Henriette's carriage had called for Ernestine.

It was close to four in the afternoon. As they played, unaware of anything except their music, the rain gradually ceased and the sun came out. It brightened the room, throwing a pool of yellow atop the piano, and at the same time serving as a tonic to cure Clara's depression. Before long she was fully infected by her father's joyful spirit and was smiling up at him as they met in unity, not only the rhythmic cadences of the music but its rich meaning as well. If only life could always be like this! And why not? Here was a singing throughout her entire body which could always be hers. It was her gift, her heritage, the very essence of her being. How fortunate she was, and how wonderful to be able to create and translate not alone, but in fullest unity with her father.

Suddenly, however, there was an abrupt end to this happiness. A clatter of wheels brought unexpectedly the return of Henriette's carriage and Ernestine and Schumann together were coming up the walk. She could hear Ernestine's voice assurring Schumann that he could stay as long as he liked. Clara and everyone else would be delighted he had come.

Trembling with emotion at the sound of their voices, she could barely see the notes in front of her. "What are you doing there, Clara?" her father cried out, carrying on with his end of the playing as she missed her accompaniment.

"Oh, I don't feel like playing any more," she threw out at him, and suddenly brought both hands down upon the keys in her jealous fury. Breaking away from the piano, she ran as quickly as she could out of the room and up the stairs.

Schumann, who had opened the door at that moment, caught only a glimpse of her bobbing curls as she disappeared. "Where is Clara off to in such a hurry?" he asked Wieck, who, unused in these later years to such scenes of temperament in his daughter, stood gaping.

Wieck threw up his hands. "She dashed out of here so fast, I didn't have time to ask her. Well, make yourselves comfortable, you two. My wife will be back before long. I was just about to take a stroll down to the market."

But his mind had been alerted by the incident. He had caught a glimpse of Clara's distraught face before she fled, and the ecstatic expressions worn by Ernestine and Schumann when they came in had given him a clue. As he walked out of the house, pulling his hat down, his face beneath was a study of concentration. "Well, well," he said to himself after a few moments of thought. "It just might be possible." And then, despite himself, he smiled, pulling thoughtfully at his chin. "Imagine it, my little Clara!" It was ludicrous, out of all proportion to the girl's usual sensible behavior, but then, who was to account for human nature? Clara was an artist, after all, and despite that solid little frame of hers, there were sensitive undercurrents. She was much too young for being seriously in love, but such a nature as hers could be capable of wild jealousy, he thought, especially under the circumstance of having had this older man for a friend for so many years. Perhaps Clementine had been more sensible than he realized when she suggested that it was high time to put a stop to Clara's walking off alone with Schumann. Those episodes must have gone to Clara's head, and the foolish girl had somehow come to the conclusion that Schumann was hers exclusively and not entitled to a friendship with any other girl.

"Nevertheless, I must help her out," he told himself. "I can't stand by and allow my girl's pride to be injured."

At dinner that evening he told Clementine that he had decided to send Clara off at once to Dresden in order for her to study composition with Herr Reissiger. Clementine was astonished by the news. It meant for her, especially at this inconvenient time, a whole business of preparing Clara for a trip. But then, Friedrich probably thought it best for his daughter to be absent when the child was born.

Ernestine, caught up with unconscious guilt, protested that it was unfair to send Clara away from her.

"Never mind, Ernestine," Clara quickly cut in. "You'll do well enough now without me. Father has been promising for a long time to let me study with Reissiger. I had better not refuse now, or I won't be given the chance again."

She did not look up at her father as she said this, for there was only a smattering of truth in her explanation. But one thing was very clear. Despite the fact that not a word concerning the incident of the afternoon had passed between them, father and daughter understood one another.

THIRTEEN

SCHUMANN did not see Clara before she left. When Ernestine told him the news, he smiled. "Isn't that just like the old man to pack Clara off to study in the midst of all this beautiful summer? He never leaves her alone."

"I thought you approved of him," Ernestine replied, puzzled by something hostile in his tone.

"Approve?" Schumann raised his brows quizzically. "One doesn't exactly approve of Wieck, one is simply grateful. I can still remember Clara as a wide-eyed little thing barely able to reach the keys. Her father was always there taking great pains with her and doing a splendid job. Still, one wishes at times she were not shackled to him in quite the way she is. There must come a time when an artist is free to try his own way. I dream now and then that Clara and I are in Zwickau, on top of a little hill we call Bridge Mount. She is laughing, her eyes are shining, and her hair is flowing loose . . . no father anywhere there. Only Robert Schumann."

Ernestine studied his face thoughtfully, then lowered her eyes. "Do you dream of Clara often?" she asked in a low voice.

They were at the Voigt estate, sitting under the trees. In the distance a small group of Henriette's friends were playing at lawn tennis, but Ernestine and Schumann had refused this pleasure for the greater one of talking alone in privacy. Schumann was intoxicated with these carefree afternoons, but love, as he had confessed to Henriette in Ernestine's presence, was not interfering with his composing. If only this summer could go on and on—

He lifted Ernestine's chin, lights of amusement flickering in his brown eyes. "How coyly you asked that," he said, forcing her to look at him. "Are you jealous that I should dream of a little girl who often sat on my knees for fairy tales? But never mind. Foolish as it may be, I know now you truly love me."

"I did not mean to love you," she confessed, no longer playing a game with him. "I told Clara many times how it was in Asch, how I had suitors enough there and was not interested in her friend Schumann. But I betrayed her after all. She's changed these past weeks. She was so quiet just before she went away, I almost had the feeling—" She paused, afraid to go on.

"But you're so solemn, Ernestine! Is it really Clara who causes such a look?"

For the first time in her young years Ernestine von Fricken was uncertain of her joyful destiny. There was a shadow here somewhere. She sensed it and was behaving instinctively rather than with clear perception. "I had the feeling," she said quietly, "that though it was Clara who was leaving, it was I, really, who was deserting her. And I cannot help but think that in the end I shall be paid back dearly for it."

Schumann looked at her incredulously. "By Clara? What puzzle are you manufacturing in that pretty head of yours? How could you imagine that Clara, with her simple heart, could ever harm you?"

"Oh, it won't be Clara necessarily," she said with a sigh. "But please, let's not talk of this any more."

Nor would she explain herself further despite all his pleas, and the unfinished conversation spoiled the day for both of them. Complaining of a headache, she went home earlier than she had intended. There a lonely room waited for her,

and she kept herself shut in until supper, trying to account
for the things she had said to Schumann and the strange suspicions that had begun to stir as a result of their conversation.
She was more seriously in love with him than she had anticipated. Her fancies had already led her to considering what
life with him in marriage would be like. She now had all her
thoughts centered upon *that* and saw for herself no permanent
happiness ever without him. In so many little ways he had
led her to believe he felt the same. There had been times,
when he kissed her, that she trembled with joy in his arms to
hear him say that he would go to any lengths to have her.
But now she felt only deep misgivings when she recalled how
he had said of Clara *and there is no father anywhere there, only
Robert Schumann.* What did he mean? When he spoke in
such a fashion she felt like an intruder between them. Yes, it
was foolish, perhaps, to be jealous of Clara, but she could
wonder—and worry. And she was doing that now.

Clara was faring better in Dresden. Almost at once she was
caught up in a social whirl more extravagant than any she
had ever previously experienced. A few concentrated hours
each morning were devoted to her studies with Reissiger, but
afterward he (who had been so advised by Wieck) left her
free to enjoy many invitations which had been pre-arranged.

It was almost as though some miracle had exchanged her
with another Clara Wieck, a Clara like any other, under no
pressures, urged on only to enjoyment. She was pensively
grateful at first but was soon genuinely caught up in high-
spirited fun. She looked forward to sunup and dressing, to
her session with Herr Reissiger, this preceding a walk in the
park with a group of young friends. There was dancing in
the afternoon, with pleasant dinners followed by outdoor band
concerts and long strolls home in the dark.

But more important was the relationship which had sprung

up between herself and a young musician whom she met at the Reissigers'. He was Carl Banck, a friend both of Schumann and her father, whose name was not unfamiliar to her, as he was also a contributor to Schumann's magazine. He was a pleasant young man, exceptionally attractive, who seemed not in the least concerned that she was a year or two younger than the other girls with whom he had become acquainted in Dresden. She first became significantly conscious of him at the evening band concerts, where he often sat staring at her, and if she deliberately met his eye, he smiled as if in invitation. There was something frightening in all this, yet his obvious admiration of her taught her to place a new value upon herself. She soon began to meet his glances more boldly, and before long found herself drawn into a flirtation.

He was about Schumann's age, ambitious, though somewhat self-centered, to Clara's regret. Yet he was thoughtful of her, making it his business to walk close by her side when they were out with a group of young people, taking her arm to help her over obstacles in the road, scolding her in a possessive tone at the slightest frown or melancholy. For a heart grieving as hers did for Schumann's neglect, all these little attentions only delighted her the more. Perhaps Carl was sincere, perhaps not. As for herself, she knew she could not, in any deeper sense, transfer her affection, but she was willing to try.

On the eighth of June, however, Carl Banck was far from her mind. It was Schumann's birthday and Clara meant to celebrate it after her own fashion. She refused all invitations and remained indoors to practice and to write letters. She thought for a long while what to say in greeting to Schumann for it was difficult to overlook that this was the first time he had not written to her during a long absence from Leipzig. Probably by now he had forgotten her altogether.

She decided finally on a teasing tone which would be

reminiscent of the days when she was still an innocent little
girl who did not comprehend the meaning of the love she
had in her heart for him. Better that he not discover the sorrow he was causing her.

Dear Herr Schumann:—Today, Sunday the 8th of June, the day
you were born, I sit here writing to you, although I have had two
invitations for this afternoon. First, let me send you my greetings,
these being: that you not always behave in a contrary way, that
you drink less Bavarian beer and not always stay behind when
others get up to go; that you stop turning night into day and
vice versa, and that you sometimes show your friends you think
of them. May you continue to write for your journal, Herr En-
thusiast, because your readers wish it, compose industriously and
firmly resolve to come to Dresden, etc.

Seriously, Herr Schumann, how can you permit yourself to
show so little attention to a friend that you do not even write to
her? Every time the post arrives I hope to get a letter, but ah!
I am disappointed. Well, one must take things as they come . . .
Still mayn't I beg for an original (but not illegible) little letter?
This wise, original and witty letter recommends to your attention
in all deliberation (as you don't like hurry)

Your friend,

Clara Wieck
Clara Wieck (*Doubleganger*)

She smiled pensively over the signature. It would remind
him of those early childhood days when he used to gather her
brothers and herself about his knee after supper and frighten
her especially with his imaginary tales of *Doublegangers*—
ghosts and wraiths. But there really were two Claras now,
she thought, the one before Ernestine, and this new one, a

ghost indeed as far as Schumann was concerned, for even when she stood before his very eyes, grown-up enough to love him, he did not see her.

Two days later she received news from home—the new baby had arrived at last—a half-sister for her, to be called Cäcilia. Her father instructed her to return to Leipzig in time for the christening on the twenty-fifth.

She left Dresden with reluctance, for the wound she bore had barely had time to heal. Yet there was a kind of relief in seeing once again all the familiar landmarks in Leipzig, the neat stone fronts of the houses, the throbbing market, the housewives out with their baskets. Above the Gewandhaus a threatening storm had piled thick masses of heavy black clouds, but there was an opposing field of blue close by through which a dauntless sun continued to try its strength. She did not fail to observe the parallel. Like the sun, she must put on a brave show despite her troubles.

Her father was in a furious state of excitement. He insisted on being the one to show Clara her new sister. He put Cäcilia's little clenched fist into his wide, strong palm and gave Clara a look charged with deep feeling. "How well I remember when I first held your fist in mine, Clara. What a sensation came over me. It was as if God had sent me a challenge. Those tight little fingers of yours were meant for something more than combing out a doll's hair, I told your mother. But she—well, never mind. I proved right in the end." His face had gradually changed as he spoke, the cheeks drawn inward, almost angrily. "This time," he said, looking down at the sleeping infant, "I will meet with no opposition. Cäcilia too will be a *Wunderkind*."

Clara kissed the tiny red face, peeping from its nest of blankets, preferring to remain silent whenever her father

spoke in this way about the mysterious quarrel which had
gone on between him and her mother. How simply he looked
at life, as if all one had to do was to lift a newborn child from
its crib and decide there and then its future. One thing was
certain. Should Cäcilia ever choose to follow a star of her
own, she would certainly have a strong opponent, for her
father seldom failed to accomplish the things he set out to do.

She left him still bending over the child, and with Alwin
and Gustav close at her heels, returned to the room below,
where Clementine and Ernestine were discussing plans for
the christening. There was an easy intimacy in their tone
together, that seemed pleasing to Clementine. While she
had been away in Dresden, Clara thought, this relationship
must have had quick, satisfying development. Almost as soon
as she came in, however, Ernestine found an excuse to break
off her conversation with Clementine, and persuaded the two
boys to allow their sister and herself to have some time alone.
Together, arm in arm, the two girls then went up to the room
they had once so enjoyed.

"You must stay now, Clara," Ernestine begged, "and never
leave me alone here again. I won't hear of your returning to
Dresden. Besides, your father says that when you were here
to help me practice, I did much better at the piano."

"But you have not been so much alone, Ernestine. And
you have friends who are far more competent than I."

Ernestine blushed. "They don't replace you, Clara. When
I come home at night to our room, there is no light, no dear
Clara waiting up to hear all my stories. I missed you very
much. Oh, how long ago it seems since I first came up these
steps. So much has happened—"

It was clear to Clara that Ernestine was troubled. Her eyes
and voice did not meet in mutual happiness. If only they
could both speak frankly about that which was uppermost

in their minds instead of the foolish gossip which they now began to exchange. But there was a fence between them, one which neither of them desired. Still, since they had not been able to communicate to one another the reasons for its erection, they did not know how to begin to tear it down.

Clara closely observed her rival, and Ernestine too, who had not usually the depth of observation to be so perceptive, was sharply aware that Clara, in her short interval away, had changed.

"He will not, he *cannot*, love her long," Clara was thinking, reconfirming in her mind Ernestine's underlying shallowness.

"She loves him and does not wish me to have him," was what Ernestine had in mind.

On the day of the christening, Schumann came, faultlessly dressed for the occasion. Upon greeting Clara he took hold of her two hands, saying, "Ah! Here is little Clara who warns me against too much Bavarian beer." He grinned. "But your other advice was easier to take. No sooner did I receive your message than I set down two new little songs. . . ."

"Only you did not write to me," she said accusingly, but with a covering smile.

He did not reply, for his gaze was already elsewhere. At the top of the stairs Ernestine stood smiling at them. She was dressed in bridal white, carrying in her hands a small bouquet of blue flowers. Behind her came Clementine, baby in arms.

"The child is so good," Clementine said cooingly, presenting her precious bundle for Schumann's inspection. "Not a whimper out of her. Consider yourself fortunate, Herr Schumann, to stand godfather for such a one."

Ignoring her feeble protests, Schumann took the baby from her, humming a melody as he rocked it back and forth. It was this scene which greeted Wieck when he came out from his study.

"Coming events cast their shadows before them, eh, Schumann?" he asked, smiling broadly.

With a click of disapproval at her husband, Clementine quickly retrieved the child. "For shame, Friedrich," she said, glancing at Ernestine. "You make the girl blush." But she could not refrain from adding her own word on the subject. "They *do* make a pair of handsome godparents for the little one, don't they, Clara?"

Ernestine and Robert godparents for baby Cäcilia! Clara looked on incredulously. Why had no one thought to tell her this news? No wonder the two of them looked so radiant. They were to stand together in church in a little while, and they did indeed look like bride and groom.

Later, as she stood in the shadows of St. Matthew's, it was not easy for Clara to watch the ceremony. The girl at Schumann's side was not an illusion, but reality. And Schumann, fully seeing the reality, was whole-heartedly accepting it. So there was no reason any longer to hope—or to wait. She must, from this day forth, face her own reality, and learn to live without joy.

But isn't destiny cheating us both? she thought. *Yes, Schumann is bound to discover me one day—only too late. He will look into my eyes then and know for whom he was really meant—*

Nevertheless she managed to exchange pleasantries with him on the way home, and with Ernestine too, who sat opposite her in the carriage. But she felt much like the swan who, though sailing boldly in the pond, is only covering with its exquisite wings the fragments of a fragile pride.

FOURTEEN

Toward dusk one late August evening, Schumann emerged from his house and set out for the Rosenthal where he had an appointment to meet his roommate, Ludwig Schunke. They were to dine at Brandt's, a favorite open-air café. It was a fine evening, thin pink clouds rapidly dissolving into fringed ribbon streamers across the sky. He walked quickly, going over in his mind a problem which had been deeply perplexing him and which he meant to put to Ludwig.

From time to time, in the intensity of his silent arguments, he unconsciously made a sweeping gesture with his hand, causing certain of the homeward bound tradespeople to turn and look after him. One of these, a stodgy gentleman whom Schumann accidentally brushed against, accosted him angrily. "See here, now. Who do you think you're pushing! I'm not used to it, you know." The man's manner was so threateningly pugnacious that the bewildered Schumann, after a stammered apology, quickly crossed to the opposite side of the street. Here he fared little better, for two haughty-looking ladies who had witnessed his previous embarrassment added the embellishment of epithets of their own: Madman! Deranged drunkard! Such people ought to stay at home where they belonged!

The peace-loving Schumann, whose mind was already perturbed enough, crossed their path with quivering jaw and proceeded as steadily as he could out of hearing. Since scenes of violence or unrestrained temper always filled him with horror, he continued his journey now in a deeply depressed mood, and at a much slower pace.

At Brandt's he discovered Ludwig sitting at a corner table already enjoying a flask of beer. "You order dinner for both of us," he said, wiping beads of perspiration from his face. "I'm in a terrible state of nerves—"

Ludwig signaled for the waiter and after giving their order, turned his full attention to the uneasy Schumann. "What's this talk of nerves? Yesterday you were soaring with happiness."

"Happiness? Good gracious, Schunke. You've no idea how miserable happiness can make a man. I didn't sleep all night."

Ludwig laughed. He had a tall, thin frame and bony, drooping shoulders. Like Schumann, he spent most of his time composing or at the piano, and a fire seemed to be burning deep in his eyes. "That, my dear friend, is the kind of misery every man should have," he said.

Schumann was too immersed in himself at the moment to detect a note of sadness in his companion's voice.

"No. Take me seriously, Ludwig. I'm near collapse from the weight of it. Last night I distinctly heard Ernestine whisper 'marry me.' "

"But my dear Schumann! I thought that was exactly what you wanted."

"Yes, yes," Schumann moaned, wiping his brow again, "but wanting it and going through with it— My God! How final it will be."

Ludwig's fine, slender nose arched sensitively. "Final, yes," he said thoughtfully, "but still life goes on—"

He lowered his eyes and drummed the cloth with his lean fingers. This was apparently a day of crisis for both of them. How ironic that Schumann should come to him now, trembling to his marrow at the thought of life-struggle—the responsibility of marriage, the immeasurable boundaries of love—while he, having been told by his doctor this very noon that he was in the last stage of consumption, could anticipate for himself only one bride, one who waited with impatience to lead him into darkness. Even now, this very moment, he could hear in his hollow chest her beckoning voice.

"You know the girl," Schumann was saying. "You've watched her often at the Voigts'. For heaven's sake, Ludwig, tell me what I should do. Consider! It will be a good match in many ways."

The waiter brought their food and both men fell to silent eating. The pink which had suffused the evening earlier was now overcome by darkness. Already the days were growing shorter. Two young servant boys came out to light the lamps. The café, in the new light, took on a less boisterous hum. Laughter and talk were subdued.

In the silence which had a fullness of its own at Schumann's table, the two friends hardly looked at one another. Their friendship was of short duration, Ludwig having been in Leipzig less than a year. But it was the best either had yet experienced. Neither of them was inclined to open confession or small confidences. Their talk, except when relaxing over a game of billiards, usually ran to Schumann's journal, music or philosophy. Indeed, this was the first occasion on which such a personal matter had come up between them, and it posed for both a certain embarrassment.

It was only with difficulty that Schumann, who gradually began to feel better once he had eaten, resumed the conversation. He lit a cigar. "What a fool I make of myself. It is not so serious, after all."

"Have you met the father?"

"No. But Wieck is working in my behalf. He showed me

a letter von Fricken sent cautioning Ernestine not to make a spectacle of herself, to play duets with me, but not, on any account, to visit me unchaperoned." Schumann smiled. "That was all. I understand there have been other letters back and forth. The baron knows, I presume, as much as Wieck thought wise to tell him."

"He might consider it beneath the girl's station to marry a musician of our class. Have you thought of that, Schumann?"

"Yes. But the curious thing is that Ernestine is so unspoiled, so unlike what you might imagine a girl of such a background to be. She never speaks 'with the tongue of the nobility' as someone put it. Her desires are all quite simple, as though she doesn't expect too much and is grateful for whatever she has. It's Henriette's opinion she's been encouraged to marry whomever she chooses—within reason of course."

"So you are fortunate then," Ludwig said. "You have only to make up your mind and say the word."

"The word!" Schumann nearly groaned again. "Until last night, I hoped for nothing else. A lovely girl, a handsome dowry. Why not? But I was thrown into panic with her sudden 'marry me.' I began to ask myself: Who is she? What have I to do with her? Love, yes . . . but do I really want marriage at this time? I trembled for my very soul . . . for my music."

"I cannot advise you," Ludwig said. "Love, beauty, dowry —shall I tell you to give them up? Who am I?"

"You are my friend," Schumann pleaded. "I have respect for your opinion. What do you think of the girl?"

"She laughs a great deal."

"Is that all?"

"She's pretty and she seems genuinely devoted to you."

"Nothing more?" Schumann asked impatiently.

Ludwig laughed and threw up his hands. "Life is short, dear Schumann. I may tell you today 'Marry this girl!' and tomorrow not be around to take the responsibility for my words. Such advice is easy. What would I do if I were in your shoes—?" He shrugged. "A good wife brings many children, a bad wife can do the same. There can be troubles, financial or spiritual, no matter how a musician chooses. But each man has to decide for himself."

"I don't require too much for happiness," Schumann reasoned, "peace in my house, love at my hearth, above all the security to pursue my music. . . ."

"No, not too much," Ludwig said with a smile. "What simple fellows we are, we musicians." He pushed back his chair. "Shall we walk?"

Schumann agreed and they strolled through the tree-lined paths, puffing at their cigars. Schumann, Ludwig reflected, had always evidenced a great deal more enthusiasm for life than he did, was always in the thick of things, finding interest in everything that went on in the world about him. In his more flamboyant or "Florestan" mood, as he himself termed it, his buoyancy sufficed for the two of them, Ludwig leaning lightly on the oars. But there were occasions, such as this one, when Ludwig wished he had longer to live so that he might be always at hand to bolster Schumann when he needed him. Schumann's genius gave him the strength of two men when there was something he believed in and wanted to accomplish, but he had also the gentleness and the vulnerability of a child in his emotional ties. This characteristic, coupled with his lack of perceptiveness in judging his fellows, could cause him no end of trouble in future years.

Are not the constant crises accompanying creativity, the self-doubt, despair, even the pain of triumph, more than enough for one man to bear, Ludwig thought. But Schumann, who could not stay out of the mainstream of life, would take on other pains and it saddened Ludwig to think how ill-prepared his companion was to suffer "the slings and arrows of outrageous fortune."

After their stroll, the two friends returned together to their lodging. Schumann said nothing more about his problem. He felt a sense of relief now that he had opened his heart on the subject. He determined on a course of action—to remain away from the Wiecks for a while and give himself time in solitude to consider Ernestine. Perhaps it was only natural for the spontaneity of his immediate affection for her to be followed by this more sober reflection.

Meanwhile he had plenty to keep him busy. He must copy out his variations on the Chopin *Nocturne* and begin to jot down ideas for his first sonata which had already started to take form in his mind. Articles and reviews had to be gathered for the journal and there were many of its organizational details still to be solved. Work! He did not mind it. It gave him joy, a sense of well-being. The more reason for not allowing the question of marriage to distract him too long. One way or another, the thing must be settled. Yes! A quick decision was what was needed. When next he saw his precious girl he would already have made up his mind.

FIFTEEN

IMMEDIATELY following the christening, Clara had returned to Dresden, but she did not remain long. A pair of charity concerts to be played in Leipzig the latter part of September brought her home again. Along with Chopin's *Fantasia* with orchestra and his *Rondo in E flat*, she was to play a new composition of Schumann's, the *Toccata*, which he had dedicated to Ludwig Schunke. He had written her a short letter expressing keen anticipation of that event, and during her stay in Dresden she labored endlessly over his work, so as not to disappoint him in her performance. She did not even allow herself the leisure to see Carl Banck, who had maintained his interest in her and was pressing constantly for an invitation.

The first news with which Clementine greeted her on her arrival (and for this she was prepared) was that Ernestine and Schumann were secretly engaged—secret, that is, from the baron. She expected to find Ernestine glowing with happiness, but she discovered her friend sitting listlessly at the window, her eyes swollen from crying. Was this the reward of love? How different Ernestine looked now from the high-spirited girl who had arrived last April! Taciturn, Ernestine showed negligible interest in Clara's return, nor would she reply to any of her solicitous questions.

Clementine, however, was a fount of information. It was Schumann, she said, who had made a mess of things. Suddenly, and without explanation, he had stopped calling on Ernestine, which had put the poor girl almost out of her mind. She would neither eat nor sleep, nor do anything worthwhile, only wander like a ghost through the house.

"We tried our best to cheer her," Clementine went on, "but no, nothing mattered to her any more, only Schumann. Your father then decided to reveal the entire affair to the baron."

"But I don't understand," Clara interrupted. "You say they are engaged—"

Clementine was enjoying the telling of her little love drama. She smiled. "Yes, so they are. We had no sooner sent off the fatal letter to the baron than Schumann made himself heard. He sent Henriette to fetch Ernestine to him, and upon her return that evening, the girl was very much herself again. Schumann had worked a miracle. I soon had it out of her that the two of them had exchanged rings and promised themselves to one another forever."

She paused to give attention to little Cäcilia who had begun to turn restlessly in her crib, while Clara, barely able to contain her emotion, waited with impatience for her to go on. "Now," said Clementine finally, "we have had a letter from the baron this very day forbidding Ernestine to stir from the house or to see Schumann again. He suspects the affair has gotten entirely out of hand and is coming here at once to remove his daughter from Leipzig—and from Schumann."

"But Father can help Ernestine, can't he, by arranging a meeting between the baron and Schumann? I'm sure, once everything is explained, there won't be any reason for the baron to take her away or to cancel the engagement."

"Your father feels he has interfered enough already," Clementine replied, "and this affair has cost him a pupil, no thanks to Schumann." She was looking at Clara curiously. A long time ago, she had begun to suspect how it was with her regarding Schumann, and she wondered now if the moistness in the girl's eyes was genuine pity for Ernestine's troubles, or pity for herself. She could not resist prodding.

"But I should think *you*, for one, would want to leave things as they stand, dear Clara. I should think you wouldn't care . . ."

"Care? Of course I care!" Clara cried out passionately. "What a hateful thing to say!"

Clementine was immediately regretful. "Never mind, you mustn't take me so seriously, child. . . ."

But Clara was already storming out of the room. This house was not a welcoming haven any more, and today especially it seemed a wretched place. Her father had not been home to greet her, and her two brothers were still in school. There had been only Clementine with her awful insinuation. Oh, no, she would never care for her stepmother, never!

Her face burned with shame. It was clear now that Clementine guessed her secret. Perhaps she had even told it to Schumann and he and Ernestine had laughed together about it at one of their rendezvous.

Rushing downstairs, she pushed open the door of the music room, and stood for a moment staring at the two large pianos. Except for the angry beating of her own heart, how uncannily quiet it was here when the keys were silent. With the windows still covered and the red plush carpet showing only a thread of light, one might think it a sanctuary, a retreat for prayer. She closed the door behind her and stood leaning against it, gratefuly absorbing the silence. Peace of mind, peace of heart —was it possible to find them any more? The sun was shining today, and out there, walking in it, were carefree people. Why could it not be the same for her? Quickly, almost frantically, she walked to the window and threw back the thick drapery.

In an instant the brightness of morning flooded the room.

I'll wait here for Father, she thought. *I'll beg him to do something to help Ernestine and Schumann.* She pressed her hands against her burning cheeks, thinking of Clementine's coolly cruel words—"I should think *you* wouldn't care, Clara."

"I care, I care, I care!" Clara suddenly cried aloud, and, bursting into tears, fell across the stiff little leather couch. Somewhere in her garden a nightingale was singing but she could not hear it.

SIXTEEN

OF ALL THOSE involved in the affair, Wieck was most relieved when Ernestine finally went home to Asch.

"We do not miss her at all," he wrote in his diary, "for in the past few weeks she has become quite a stranger in our home and has lost all her amiability and naturalness. Besides she has forgotten practically everything that has been taught to her with so much difficulty. She is like a green plant scorched by the sun—that is to say, by Schumann."

But the removal of Ernestine from Leipzig by Baron von Fricken created something near to frenzied desperation in Schumann. He could think of nothing except to recapture his pretty prey. He went in hot pursuit after father and daughter, forgetting all previous commitments, even, to her profound sorrow, Clara's concert. In Zwickau, where the von Frickens had stopped for a change of horses, Schumann finally caught up with them. He carefully watched for an opportune moment when the baron's back was turned before making his presence known to Ernestine. Once holding her in his arms, all past hesitations and doubts were obliterated under the pressure of forbidden love. In this stolen moment, the hastily exchanged kiss was sweeter than it had ever been. Seeing that Ernestine was crying, Schumann swore to her that this separation would be only temporary.

"As soon as the baron has had time to recuperate from his temper," he said ardently, "I'll go to him and make my position clear. By Christmas, surely, he'll think better of all this. You'll see, dear Ernestine, we shall be happy again!"

Ernestine was only too eager to listen to these reassuring words and to believe. She dried her tears, and by the time her father returned, was a model of composure. As her carriage pulled away toward Asch, she looked longingly toward Schumann, who had drawn himself into the shadows, and gave him a smiling signal of courage.

Schumann, however, felt emotionally drained. The events of the past two days had been so swift that he had hardly had time to think. Now, as he began his journey homeward, the full effect of his wild chase to Zwickau took hold of him. All his excitement and previous exhilaration suddenly subsided into melancholic depression. He was, in fact, deeply puzzled by his behavior. Could he not just as easily have knocked on Wieck's door the night of the baron's arrival and presented himself, credentials in hand? The baron, from reputation, was not an unreasonable man. He might have been willing to listen to a proposal.

"Well, another two months is not such a long time to wait," he consoled himself wearily. Suddenly his thoughts went to the missed concert and to his *Toccata*. How had Clara brought it off, he wondered. If anyone had told him a few months ago that one of his pieces was to have its first public performance and he not there to hear it—!

But love, too, had its strong pull. He thought of Heine's verse.

> I've loved you, and love you this very hour!
> And though the whole world crashes,
> Still the flames of my love will tower
> Over the cities' ashes.

Yes, it was like that. But tonight he was not so fond of love. He was incredibly tired, and there was no singing inside of him.

The next two months proved crucial ones. He was plagued on all sides by problems and hardly in an emotional state to cope with them. His head was bursting with ideas for new compositions, but his time at the piano was interrupted more often than he liked by details in connection with his magazine. There were difficulties with the present publisher, Hartmann, and negotiations were in process to hand over the publication to the firm of J. A. Barth. Of its original enthusiastic launchers, few of the journal's staff were on hand to pull their end of the job. Julius Knorr, theologian turned musician, who had at first officially been announced as editor, was ill; but even before his illness Schumann, behind the scenes, had played the major role in this capacity. Wieck, who was skeptical of Schumann's business acumen, and who had promised his assistance only if Schumann truly proved himself industrious in the venture, was not around to give advice. He had taken Clara off on tour, and accompanying them was one other who might have been of aid, the energetic Carl Banck. Wieck, it seemed, had lately taken Banck under his wing, entrusting to him Clara's voice training, a fact which for the moment was of little subjective interest to Schumann.

Then there was Ludwig Schunke, also removed from the scene, the gravity of whose illness was now only too plain. Here Schumann was suffering more than just the loss of a trustworthy aide: his best friend was dying.

When Ludwig, who came from a family of musicians, had first arrived from Stuttgart in March of the previous year, introducing himself to Wieck's circle of young admirers,

Schumann had heard an inner voice say, "Here he is, the one for whom we have been waiting." Yet, as he knew now, Ludwig was destined to be only a temporary recruit, bringing his gifted musicianship into the Leipzig orbit for a brief moment, and leaving almost as quickly as he had come.

In the beginning Schumann had foreseen something extraordinary for them both. They took lodgings together and he wrote, assuring his mother, ". . . he is an excellent man and friend, ever zealously striving after all that is finest and best. . . . I could do without all other friends for this one alone."

The Voigts moved Ludwig into their home in order to guarantee him the best of attention, and it was there Schumann saw and resigned himself to the inevitable. He found himself plunged into uncontrollable melancholy, obsessed by his recurrent dread of illness and death. Funerals too filled him with terror, and realizing that he would not be able to endure witnessing Ludwig's final release of life, he once more fled to that haven of his childhood, his mother's house in Zwickau.

It was December now. The Mulde was not yet frozen, but the mountains of Zwickau thrust dark, spinescent trees skyward, and the fields below were preparing themselves for snow. Schumann looked in vain for symbols of comfort. He thought of his promise to Ernestine but he knew he could not make a move in her direction until he had final news of Ludwig. One ran away, yes, but even so there must eventually be a time for knowing. And was not one always listening for the dreaded word even while tightly cupping the ears against it?

"How can I bear the thought of giving him up?" he wrote to Henriette. "If he dies, for heaven's sake, do not write it to me, or let someone else write. . . ."

Schumann knew well every pond, every public garden, every

ancient building of Zwickau. Here were the scenes of his childhood. In 1812, 150,000 of Napoleon's soldiers had marched through these streets on their way to Russia, and vivid in his memory were the tales his father had told him of the French grenadiers. Now, in his grim time of waiting, he sought to recapture something of those golden days when his father was still alive. He took long, solitary walks in the direction of the wooded hills they both had loved, returning in the end to stand for awhile in silence under the Gothic structure of St. Katherine's.

But most dear to him was the Cloth Hall (Gewandhaus) with its familiar gables. It was here he came after receiving news of Ludwig's death, seeking it out as a sanctuary one sleepless morning, while around him still the deserted market place lay slumbering in a shroud of wintry mist. Grief-stricken, he stood alone, facing the gray silence of the building from which so often in the past he had heard the music of the great masters. But gradually he was not alone, nor was the Gewandhaus empty of sound. Such moments as these, when your town is sleeping, and you alone in the dawn give life to an empty street, can sharpen your senses to the point of uncanny power. The solitary child will spread apart his tiny fingers and transform them to the fingers of a giant; he rules the morning, he creates the world. The solitary man suffers his giant hand to reduce to the size of a child's; he summons the past and walks willingly in his father's shadow.

It was like this now for Schumann. He could hear muffled drums and high, clear horns, a great swelling of melody crying through these crevices, violins whose passionate intensity made him reach for the warm hand of his father. August Schumann, now vivid and alive, a light of culture for his nine-year-old son, understood the gesture and responded. He was no musician. He had begun his manhood as a grocer, but he had dreamed

of finer trades, of writing novels, of becoming a publisher of
books. In the end he had realized both dreams. Now he
would nurture the dream of his son.

Together they listened, the boy's eyes bright with the
hearing, the father's proud and rejoicing in the joy of his
son. Afterward they walked in the sunlight of Zwickau lanes.
"Father," said the boy, "may I have an orchestra of my own?
Herr Kuntzsch will help us, but we need scores, supplies. . . ."
Johann Kuntzsch, organist, was Robert's piano teacher. He
had told the father, "One day that boy will outstrip me."

"If that is what you really want, boy, then that is what
you shall have and 'bring forth your music into the air,' as
Shakespeare said. I was never a man to hold back talent. As
long as I live, you shall have everything you need—"

The boy heard melodies. He lifted his head to the sky and
made of the varied textured clouds a series of ascending chords.
He raced alongside the peaceful Mulde and was in rhythm
with the song flowing out of his brain.

"The sounds are always there," he told his father. "Where
do they come from?"

The father smiled and led him home to the new Streicher
grand pianoforte standing in the parlor, bought especially to
indulge the art he saw dominant in his son. "Can you play
for me the tunes you are hearing?"

The songs were simple lines of melody flowing through
intricacies too difficult for the boy's fingers to articulate. He
tried but he could not play all that he heard.

He was dissatisfied and discouraged.

"Don't fret over it, boy. Your art, like mine, takes years
of tending before it can be what you want. You'll see. It
will grow while you are growing. Be patient, work hard, and
one day all these sounds you're hearing will find definite
places for themselves, come clearly, orderly, arranged like a

planned design out of your mind. You'll shout aloud 'wonderful! wonderful!' and in your excitement, argue that some power outside of yourself planted perfect fruit in your brain. But remember well what I say. All genius flowers out of living experience. Everything that happens to child or man, all that he sees, hears, touches, smells, will reappear when he needs it. For nothing is lost forever. So, boy! Don't be discouraged because you can't put onto the piano everything you hear. Live! Observe! Practice! Next year, or the year after, or a dozen years after, your reward will come."

Nothing is lost forever. Not the father's smile or the father's voice, or the feel of his sympathetic hand. In the ripening dawn, while the cold sun slowly erases the shadows of the market place and a closed carriage comes with its sleepy horses slowly moving through the mist, Schumann clings still to his happier times. . . .

It is 1819. He is in Carlsbad where he has gone to hear the great Moscheles play. This man, this Moscheles—can one ever reach his height? How? When? The dream is overflowing.

"May I keep the program, Father?"

"Of course. As long as you like."

"One day I'll play like Moscheles. I'll make you proud."

"Play like Robert Schumann, my son, and I'll be very proud to listen—"

Nothing is lost forever, not the father's smile, or the father's words.

"Are you listening, now, Father? Ludwig is dead—that music you hear rising out of the Gewandhaus is *my* music—I have brought it up out of my love and suffering."

"I hear it, son, and I rejoice in your gift. Doesn't the poet, Novalis, tell us: *All the hazards of life are elements out of which we can fashion whatever we like—*"

Gradually the square took on the realities of light and sound. Unfamiliar voices penetrated the morning. With shoulders hunched in the cold, Schumann walked slowly through the reviving streets. As he made the turn leading to his house, he felt suddenly a soft substance hit against his face. He looked quickly up.

Slantwise, and swiftly, like thousands of little jewels flung upon his fields, the first snow of the season had arrived.

SEVENTEEN

A FEW DAYS after Ludwig's death, Schumann made his appearance at the baron's estate in Asch. The morning was crisp and cold, smelling of pines and firewood. From a road whose summit seemed almost to touch the clean wash of fleckless blue sky, he made an entry between two majestic rows of poplars, having to walk a considerable distance before catching sight of the von Fricken house. It was an impressive palatial dwelling of true Saxon character, and Schumann, whose mind often ran to fantasy, could not help but view it as an appropriate setting for such a mission as his—the rescuing of his love from a stubborn father.

At his heels as he made his approach ran three handsome but savage-seeming hounds, against whom he had to guard frantically the safety of his coattail. Had he not felt so seriously the romantic delicacy of his visit, he might have been able to laugh at himself coming awkwardly and unannounced up the baron's path in his too conspicuously new clothes, escorted by a pack of furiously yelping dogs. But he sounded the knocker on the massive door, painfully conscious that his entire future lay inside, and that everything from this point on depended on the good will of the man to whom he was going.

He need not have been so ill at ease. The interior of the house, once he was granted admittance by the baron's man-servant, gave a far less formidable impression. The large room to which he was immediately ushered was warm and cheerful, and sitting in a most impressive light was the piano on which he was pleased to see certain of his own works, his *Allegro* inscribed to Ernestine and the *Symphonic Études* which he had composed as variations on a theme by the baron himself. These were reassuring signs, as were others in this room, of a highly cultured man, and Schumann breathed easier as he waited for the baron.

There was no sign of Ernestine. The house, except for the barking hounds outside, was extraordinarily quiet. But after a short wait, during which Schumann stood admiring the winter view of trees from the room's southerly window, the baron finally appeared. He was informally dressed and surprisingly cordial.

"You should have given me notice, my dear Schumann. I would have sent someone to fetch you in the village."

The astounded Schumann made a clumsy apology. Obviously he had been right about the cooling off period, but still this behavior on the baron's part, as if nothing unpleasant had happened between them, was puzzling. After a few moments a servant entered with hot drinks which he placed on a small table separating the two men, who were now at ease and seated.

Von Fricken, whose bald head was brightly polished, was a specimen of good health. He was solidly built though shorter of stature than Schumann, and his manner was impeccable. He had the look of a man who spent a good deal of time outdoors and who enjoyed abundant leisure. But Schumann was aware, and had been for some time, that his host was devotedly conscientious in pursuit of artistic hobbies, being an especially active participant in musical affairs. It was Ernestine who had first acquainted him with one of von Fricken's attempts at composition, and in a shrewd gesture of musical friendship, Schumann had expanded upon the theme to write his own variations—those same *Symphonic Études* now sitting on the baron's piano. The gesture had genuinely pleased von Fricken, for he and Wieck at their recent meeting had concurred in the opinion that, erratic as Schumann might seem at times, he did, without doubt, show flashes of genius. Since his return with Ernestine from Leipzig, the baron had taken time to do some serious thinking.

"Stay a few days with us, dear Schumann," he said amiably. "Do you know our countryside? It is especially exciting in winter. Do you care for hunting?"

With rather untactful haste, Schumann assured him that he did not, having no desire to participate in the slaughtering of animals. But a walk in the woods would delight him and he would enjoy joining the baron in some music making. He said nothing of Ernestine.

"Splendid! Splendid! We shall use our time beneficially for us both," the baron said smiling. "Who knows what will come of it?"

Schumann flushed slightly. "There is an important matter which brought me here, sir—if you don't mind. I thought to have a word with you on it in Leipzig, but you left so quickly—"

"I was rather in a hurry," the baron said, drawing on his pipe. "But we will have all the time we want now, dear Schumann. Why rush? I am aware that you have something more serious on your mind than rambling through Asch or hearing me on the flute. We shall talk about it after dinner."

Schumann was only too relieved to postpone the discussion. He took out his handkerchief and wiped his face, while the baron pulled a bell rope. "Show Herr Schumann to the south wing guest room," the baron said to the servant who appeared, then turned again to his visitor. "You will find it very pleasant there, my dear fellow. Everything you need for your comfort, including a piano. We dine at three. I will send my man to fetch you."

Schumann clasped the baron's extended hand and followed after the servant. His heart was beating so rapidly that he could not wait to reach the safety of the room assigned to him and there to collapse in privacy. The last person he desired to see at this moment was Ernestine herself. But there seemed no danger of this, for as he mounted the carpeted steps, there was an almost uncanny silence in the halls. He wondered if the stiffly proper servant who walked ahead of him could hear the pounding inside his chest.

"Thank God," he said to himself, "the worst is over now. The baron certainly seems kindly disposed—but in heaven's name, what am I shaking about?" At the same time he was conscious of profound relief that he still had a few hours of freedom in which to think things over, a fact which troubled him considerably and gave him cause for guilt. At the very threshold of his prospective bride, why should he continue to dwell on a letter he had received from her when he was in Zwickau, that sad, sorry little spectacle of Ernestine's brave effort to impress him with her grand ideas, but which, for the first time, had revealed to him the utter poverty of her mind? After his high praise of her, he had been ashamed to show the letter to his mother. Yet when he examined his heart carefully, he could find no other fault with her. For her beauty, for her innate goodness, he loved her well. Or did he? One curious sentence which she had interjected out of context in her letter had been repeating itself in his mind ever since: *I sometimes think you can never love anyone but Clara.* Ah, Ernestine! Why torment yourself and me too in such a fashion?

At two o'clock, after a sleep permeated with disturbing dreams, Schumann awoke. The curtains were drawn, and he lay for a few moments with his head aching, wishing that he were safely back in Zwickau. The room, as the baron had promised, was comfortable and pleasant. A crackling fire was burning in the hearth, and above the mantel hung a brilliant picture of Friedrich's. A spinet sat in the far corner catching the window light. Schumann reflected that this must be a favorite room of the baron's, there being many musical trinkets in it, such as miniature harps, delicately carved violins, and other such carefully collected valuables artistically placed on the shelves.

Slowly he roused himself, with a feeling of wonderment that he was here at all, and after refreshing himself, sat down to have a smoke before dinner. After a time he became conscious that there was a stir of life down below. He could see the figure of a young girl, dressed in a hooded winter outfit, hurrying toward a waiting horse-drawn sleigh. At her side was the baron himself, one hand on her elbow.

"Ah, he is sending her away," he said aloud, and not without disappointment, for he had just been consoling himself that one look at Ernestine's bright face at dinner would probably work its miracle and revive his enthusiasm for this adventure. Indeed, a renewed compassion for her was already stirring as he saw her step into the warmth of the sled rugs, and upon a wave of the baron's arms, go sailing downhill out of sight. Poor girl! How she must have longed to give him some signal before being forced off like this!

At dinner, the baron made no effort to conceal what had taken place. "Unfortunately," he said, nodding toward her empty chair, "we will not have the pleasure of Ernestine's company. She has gone on a visit to one of my neighbors. But don't look so glum, my dear Schumann. She will be back in a day or so and you will have time enough then to say to her whatever will be on your mind."

For the moment he seemed eager to discuss other than personal matters with his guest, and before long drew the not unwilling Schumann into a lively discussion of German affairs. There was much of political interest to talk about. In various principalities, for Germany was not a united nation but a host of individual states governed by an assortment of thirty-six kings and princes, liberals were gathering together to draw up programs calling for a German union based on the sovereignty of the people. At the time of Napoleon's march across German soil, they argued, the strong nationalism which had developed, causing the people to support the aristocracy willingly, had been useful for the defeat of Napoleon; but now, rank servility to rulers of a disunited land served only to hold back progress and to destroy the liberties of the people. Inspired by the uprisings in France, these men of vision longed for a more democratic land dedicated to the brotherhood of man, and already such ideas had begun to invigorate some of the literature pouring out of Germany. A general alarm was quickly sounded by the fearful rulers, strict censorship was imposed, freedom of assembly denied, and many outstanding leaders among the people were forced to flee with the police hot on their trail.

One of the first to fly for his safety was Heinrich Heine, poet and political pamphleteer. He crossed the Rhine on the first of May, 1831, and landing in France, proclaimed "Freedom" to be the new religion, himself as its potential high priest. His ideas were at the moment the subject of hot debate among Schumann's circle, for Heine was challenging all writers and musicians to stop living in the past, to come out of their introspective dream world and put their art at the service of their country and humanity. "Never separate politics from scholarship," he told them, "art from science; be at once artists, tribunes and apostles." Some among Schumann's friends opposed him, while others argued that he who had been forced to flee his homeland was its best defender, loving it more passionately from his exile than many among themselves who kept quiet about injustices and were continuing to publish without fear of police or censor.

The baron, though he prided himself on more liberal ideas than others of his class, now declared Heine far too acid-tongued and radical to suit him, while Schumann, who had always been an admirer of Heine's, argued well in his behalf. "I am a subscriber," he told the baron, after a few moments of heated argument, "to Heine's recent statement in the *Allgemeine Zeitung*," and he began, to the astonishment of his host, to repeat word for word one of its more controversial passages:

" 'When we have succeeded in making the greater portion of mankind understand our own times, they will no longer permit themselves to be provoked to hatred and war by the hireling scribblers of the aristocracy. The confederation of peoples—the Holy Alliance of Nations—will come into being; we shall no longer need to sustain standing armies of many hundreds of thousands of murderers because of mutual distrust; we shall use their swords and horses to plow, and we shall win peace, prosperity and freedom.' "

"Ah," said the baron with a smile. "A noble idea, no doubt. I too see its merit, but you and I, my dear friend, we are among those peaceful dreamers who will not have our skins pricked by *too* much activity for the cause. Is that not so?"

He rose, indicating his wish to conclude the debate. Schu-

mann was not sure whether, in his last remark, the baron was
passing astute judgment on his character, or, as his future
father-in-law, giving him a friendly warning.

Heine had made good dinner conversation, however, and
this led the two men in animated mood to the privacy of the
baron's quarters where they settled down for an after-dinner
smoke and talk of a more personal nature.

"We need not be evasive with one another," the older man
said, putting a light to Schumann's cigar. "Let me begin by
indicating that I was summoned to Leipzig by certain peculiarities in Ernestine's behavior, peculiarities which led me
to believe that she had not been discreet concerning this
affaire de coeur."

"Discreet, sir?" Schumann took this to be an attack upon
himself as well.

"A young girl often does foolish things," the baron said
smiling. "And you must admit, my dear Schumann, that
certain impulsive words on your part had quite turned the
girl's head. Since we did not know exactly what you had in
mind—concerning her future, I mean—the situation could
not be permitted to continue. But you have now deemed it
your duty to speak frankly, and I am not averse to hearing
what you have to say."

Despite himself, Schumann went red in the face. He
avoided the pure, steel-like glare of the baron's eyes and
reached out in memory for the comfort of Ernestine's features.
It put him into panic that he could not remember them
distinctly. He could hear, as if from afar, his own voice saying,
"Ernestine and I—we wish your approval—we wish to be
married."

"So! And you are certain of your feelings for her?"

"Yes, oh, yes. You can rest assured." Ernestine's enforced
absence had once more led Schumann to believe in himself.

"You must understand, my dear young man, that these affairs are not so simple. Ernestine, for example. You have ideas concerning her dowry?"

"I have not given much thought to it," Schumann confessed in a low voice. He was not telling the whole truth. A practical approach in these matters was considered imperative, especially in his own case, since only with a secure income could any composer hope to have the leisure to go on with his work. But still this turn in the discussion embarrassed him. He wondered if the baron thought he wanted Ernestine only for her dowry.

"Aside from your own income, which we shall discuss in a moment, you take it for granted, then, that Ernestine will bring enough to guarantee security for you both. . . ."

"I assume," Schumann replied with great discomfort, "that we will not have to concern ourselves. . . ."

"Ah!" The baron sat back and puffed away vigorously, keeping his eyes glued to Schumann's unhappy face.

"I am a musician, sir, as you know. I am not, however, exactly penniless."

"You have an income from the journal?"

"Not much. One hundred and fifty *Thalers*."

"And from your father?"

"Six thousand *Thalers*."

"I see."

"Eventually I will have a greater share of my father's estate. This, plus what Ernestine brings . . ."

"Let us get back to the original question," the baron interrupted quickly. "You are certain of your feelings for her?"

"Yes. I love her; otherwise I should not be here."

"But you have known her only a short time. Since April, I believe."

"Time is not always a factor in love," Schumann said, led

now, almost involuntarily, to heated support of his case. "Ernestine has all those fine qualities one can hope for in a wife."

"I take it then," said the baron, leaning back, "that you find her sufficiently cultivated intellectually, think her neither too impulsive, nor lacking in innate refinement . . ."

"She is your daughter, sir!" Schumann blurted out, puzzled by this line of questioning.

The baron shook his head. "My dear Schumann, that is precisely what she is not. She is unfortunately an illegitimate child whom, out of the kindness of my heart, I have brought here and raised. But you are absolutely right about her character. She is a sincere, gentle girl and will make you an excellent wife. I am delighted that you love her and want to protect her. I give you my blessing. Take her and be happy. But you must understand, of course, that under these unusual circumstances—Ernestine's not being my legal daughter, I mean—she will come to you entirely without dowry."

EIGHTEEN

The Gewandhaus in Leipzig was to have a new conductor, a young man of genius whose fame was now well established throughout Europe. He was none other than Felix Mendelssohn whom Clara had first seen in Paris.

Young Mendelssohn's arrival was awaited with intense excitement. His was the kind of star which had ascended early in his youth, steadily rising and obscured by few clouds. Unlike most of the other young musicians surrounding him, who were entirely dependent for their survival on patrons, or on long hours of teaching which tore them away from their creative labors, Mendelssohn, the banker's son, never had to fear privation. Yet part of his greatness, that which won for him the profound respect of his contemporaries in the world of music, was his selfless devotion to actively bringing the best in music, the old as well as the new, to public attention.

Seemingly strong and vigorous, Mendelssohn was exhausting himself in the number of projects in which he engaged. Schumann, who soon came to idolize him, was particularly impressed that one who could easily have enjoyed all the luxury of composing under the most ideal conditions threw himself with such energy into the mainstream of the struggle against the "Philistines." But Mendelssohn, at an early age, out of his own experience, knew what a struggle it took to defeat men of small vision whose shallow and shoddy concepts of art were so often forced upon the listening public.

He quickly found his place among those Romanticists in
Germany who were trying, though not always successfully,
to grope their way out of the mystical despairing mood which
for the past number of years had engulfed poets, musicians
and artists alike in a period of intellectual confusion and
political oppression. "The poetry of life is greater than the
poetry of death," Heine cried out to his fellow artists. Schumann's "Davidites," caught up in an ecstasy of musical creativity, heard the cry and were trying to understand it.

At the age of seventeen, in the Summer of 1826, Mendelssohn wandered happily in the beautiful gardens of his family's
Berlin estate at Number 3 Leipzigerstrasse and composed the
Midsummer Night's Dream Overture. His close-knit musical
family would have liked nothing better than to keep him there
always, protected by them in that safe luxurious world, while
he composed to his heart's content. But Mendelssohn's enthusiasm was not for an isolated garden which shut him off
from the world. He gradually broke loose from the family
bonds, and upon returning from Paris, spent three energetic
years directing all the musical enterprises in Düsseldorf. Now,
to his satisfaction, he was summoned for the same purpose
to Leipzig, and was delighted by the prospect of working in
the city which for so many years, after his appointment as
Cantor to St. Thomas' Church in 1723, had sheltered Johann
Sebastian Bach. It was here that Bach's magnificent *St.
Matthew Passion* had been born. This masterpiece had a
special place in Mendelssohn's heart for, after stubborn opposition and frustrating struggles, he had finally won for it a
performance in the Berlin *Singakademie* in March of 1829,
when he was but twenty years old. Others might be content
to allow the great music of the past to die out, but Mendelssohn, like Schumann, dreamed always of how to preserve it.

Both young men shared a dream that Germany, in recognition of Bach's genius, would one day undertake the publication of his complete works.

Mendelssohn's arrival in Leipzig in September of 1835 had great significance for Clara. She was to play at his debut on the evening of October fourth, not as soloist, but as pianist for the Beethoven *B flat Trio*. The excitement generated around her by her elders because of her part in the coming event, tended more to inspire than to awe her. She was on the eve of her sixteenth birthday and in a happier frame of mind than she had been for many months.

The previous winter had been spent on tour with her father, and wherever they went, not only was her performance widely acclaimed, but her beauty as well. Carl Banck was not the only young man who gave her adoring glances. She was suddenly conscious of more than one admirer, among them a certain cellist by the name of Müller with whom she enjoyed a brief flirtation. Indeed she had almost convinced herself that she was in love with Müller and had written very tenderly of him to Clementine. But on returning to Leipzig in April, one of the first visitors to arrive was Schumann, and she knew she had been deceiving herself.

She was standing in conversation with one of her father's pupils, a young girl by the name of Auguste, with whom she had struck up a friendship, when Schumann came in to shake hands with her father. Clara thought he looked troubled, and thinner than when she had seen him last. She could not remove her eyes from his face, but he barely gave her a glance during the whole of his conversation with Wieck. Not even on leaving did he speak to her, only managing a somewhat embarrassed nod as he passed her and Auguste.

Clara looked after him, barely able to restrain tears of

humiliation. "There is nobody whom I love as I do him," she whispered to the astonished Auguste, "and he has not so much as looked at me!"

But as the summer wore on, there was a marked change in his behavior toward her which gave her cause for much wonder. He seemed always to be studying her, looking her over as if he were truly seeing her for the first time. He went to Zwickau for a holiday and the letters she received from him contained curious, tender sentiments quite out of character, she thought, for one who was engaged to another. Ernestine had written her that, during Schumann's stay in Asch last December, her father had granted them permission for a formal engagement, and she was looking forward with joy to the day when she and Schumann would be man and wife.

What then, Clara wondered, did Schumann imply in his letter of August twenty-eighth when he addressed her so familiarly, "From the midst of all the autumn glories and exquisite skies there peeps out an angel's head which is exactly like a certain Clara whom I know well," and concluded: "You know how dear you are to me!"

Had Schumann had a change of heart concerning Ernestine? Ah, poor girl, if that were so, for her whole life was now given over to him. Yet as she read his words, trying to decipher some hidden meaning, Clara could not suppress wild surges of joy.

"I was just winding my way like a worm through your sonata which two gentlemen from Hannover wanted to hear," she wrote back to him, "when a letter came to me, and from whence, thought I? Then I read Zwickau. I was very surprised, for when you went away from here, you did not give me much hope of such a letter. For two whole hours I have been poring over it, and yet there are still a few spiteful words left which will not get into my head by any means. . . ."

When he returned to Leipzig he still gave her no explanation of those "few" words, but his look also seemed to contain some joyful secret. Whatever it was, it made her happier. She was glowing with health and beauty and everyone about her began to remark, "How radiant she is. Success doesn't seem to spoil Clara. It makes her more charming than ever."

Yes, everything was changing for the better. Even her father gave recognition to the fact that she was now a mature artist. He wrote in her diary at the time of her confirmation:

My daughter: It is time you became independent, and it seems to me of the greatest importance that you should do so. I have devoted ten years of my life to your training. Recognize the obligations you owe me; aspire always to act with generosity, disinterestedness, and all possible humanity; on all occasions practice virtue, the only true religion. That you may be misunderstood, slandered, or envied matters little. The essential thing is never to betray your principles. You will have a hard struggle, but that struggle will itself teach you supreme courage. I will always be your friend and counsellor asking for nothing better than to come to your aid.

Thus he gave her intellectual and artistic freedom. And it was in this serene mood that she practiced for the coming Mendelssohn debut. On her sixteenth birthday, Schumann's *Davidites*, as he called all those connected with his pioneering journal, organized a testimonial for her at the *Kuchengarten*. Dressed in a lovely, pale blue merino with a sheer scarf at her throat, she sat at the head of the table, Schumann directly opposite and Felix Mendelssohn smiling at her from her left. Wieck, a proud turn to his mouth, sat to her right, while Ortlepp, Carl Banck and one or two others filled up the rest of the seats. It was Schumann who had been chosen spokesman for the little band of admirers. After a few moments, he

waved with a spoon for attention. "Dearest Chiarina—" he
began, and paused, smiling sheepishly, as if words now failed
him.

"On with it! On with it!" came shouts from either side.

"We don't require poetry, just simple words," Wieck said
with a laugh, in which everyone joined. Schumann's tendency
toward flowery utterances was a common joke among them.

Schumann continued to look only at Clara. Her face was
burning under his intense gaze. "What brings us together
today," he said quietly, once the laughter had subsided, "is
something more than just to say how much we love you.
That we love you, surely you know already. No, there is
something else. We look at our Clara and see that she is no
longer that funny-serious little girl out of whom Herr Wieck
created a *Wunderkind*. We see that she is a woman, and not
just an ordinary woman, but a fellow artist whom we respect
and admire for all her very fine accomplishments in the field
to which we are all here dedicated."

An enthusiastic applause of approval came from around
the table. Mendelssohn presented her with a small, porcelain-
handled basket and urged her to look inside. With a quivering
smile of gratitude, Clara unwrapped the tissue and drew from
the depths of the basket a delicate gold watch. . . .

"Gentlemen—" she began. But she was too moved to go
on. With tears in her eyes, she turned to her father for help.

"Clara has difficulties when it comes to speech making,"
Wieck said, patting her hand. "So, gentlemen, let me invite
all of you to come to my house for dinner. Perhaps, with a
little champagne to help her along, she will then find the
right words."

It was a celebration which two, at least, of its participants
were destined never to forget. Clara and Schumann could
not foresee that it would be the last they would celebrate

together for four long troublesome years. The table was set up with the best silverware and china, the glasses filled with champagne. Wieck was not as rich a man as he would have liked to be, but he sometimes put on a feast as if he were. His guests, this thirteenth day of September, were taking advantage of it all and responding with exceptional gaiety. In the midst of their carefree chatter, Clara rang a glass with her spoon.

"Hear! Hear! Clara has something to say," Wieck shouted.

She tossed back a wisp of hair that had loosened onto her cheek and raised her glass. "Gentlemen," she said, "I cannot refrain from expressing my heartfelt thanks for the beautiful present!"

Of all those present, Mendelssohn was the most formal, but he now had a sparkle in his eye and looked as if he might open his collar. "With your permission, sir?" he asked Wieck, pointing toward the piano. "Clara deserves a reward for that fine speech."

Wieck was only too delighted. Mendelssohn rose, adjusted himself on the piano chair, and with a melancholy tilt of his head, affected a pose unlike his own. The music which then followed was so obviously an improvisation according to Chopin that his audience responded with laughter. Mendelssohn had confessed earlier at the table that he could never fit himself into that style of playing, but his imitation was remarkably faithful.

"Now, Clara," he called out to her, "guess if you can who sits at your piano now!" He struck a handsome chord, then ran into a series of little ripples, his hands leaping over one another with colorful decorations of sound, all turning upon one another in variations in a mad scramble to reach home again.

"Franz Liszt! It's Liszt!" everyone shouted at once.

"It's Liszt all right," Carl Banck put in with a laugh. "He trips all over himself."

There was an air of superiority in Carl's tone which seemed to offend Mendelssohn. "Don't belittle him," he said, turning his eyes on that young man, who was seated next to Clara. "Perhaps he is a far greater talent than any of us—impetuous at times, yes. But—a genius."

Schumann heartily agreed with Mendelssohn. He did not care for the petty jealousies which so often sprang up between one musician and another. Fun, imitation was one thing. Scorn or snobbishness not to be tolerated. His own compositions were as yet hardly known outside of this intimate circle, but his interest in all music, like Mendelssohn's, was objective. New music especially interested him, and in his journal, he continually rose to its defense, especially if, on first hearing, it was received coldly, due to unusual passages which for the moment seemed strange to the audience. "Everything that is new has spirit in it," he would argue. "Honor the old, but also meet the new with a warm heart. As for me, I cherish no prejudice against unknown names."

He had honored Mendelssohn in the past from hearsay. After today, he knew, he would love him even better at close hand.

Mendelssohn's debut took place on a cool, clear October night. The Gewandhaus sparkled with the diamonds of its wealthy patrons and the chatter of the students who filled the rear of the hall. Rumor had spread that Mendelssohn was to do away with the old tradition of sitting at the piano to direct the orchestra. He would stand on the podium and use a little stick, a baton, it was said. Until now it had always been the first violinist, watching the nods and cues from the orchestra's leader, who had passed his instructions on to the other players. But Mendelssohn preferred to be more intimate with the orchestra. He identified himself with the rising swell of sounds and experienced the keenest satisfaction in calling forth every nuance, his voice, his body, his very finger tips participating: flute, drum, violin, horn—he was all of them. He could not sit and give foolish nods. No, he must himself be an instrument of the composer.

He began with Beethoven's *Fourth Symphony*, introducing it for the first time to his Leipzig audience. This act alone openly identified him with Schumann's Davidites. He was bringing something new! He would revive the masters. A Spohr violin concerto followed, then Mendelssohn's own *Meeresstille (Calm Sea) Overture*. The trio, in which Clara was to participate, would conclude the program.

Clara sat in the first row, her father on one hand, Schumann on the other. Soon after the concert began, she felt Schumann's eyes resting on her face. He kept them there so steadily that she found herself unable to concentrate on the program. Finally she looked up at him with a puzzled, querying expression, but he turned quickly away, embarrassed, apparently, by the frankness of the question he saw in her eyes. He was deeply agitated. She had known it from the moment he took his seat beside her. It was not only the excitement of the debut, but something else— She found his nearness very disturbing.

When it came time for the trio, she rose to go to the platform, conscious that his eyes were following her all the way. "He is comparing me with Ernestine," she thought. "For weeks now he has done nothing else. Ah, how can I play my best when he sits there watching me so, studying me, tearing me apart!"

But at the same time a thrill of wonderment enveloped her. Tonight! What did it all mean? For Mendelssohn, his brilliant debut. For her, unquestionably a turning point in

her career, for this audience would be listening to her for the
first time not as Leipzig's *Wunderkind,* but as a mature artist,
Germany's most outstanding woman performer. And for
Schumann? What did tonight mean especially to him?

Clara bent her head more closely over the piano and at cue
struck her chords to echo the strings. Almost intuitively she
guessed the answer. Schumann, editor, composer, critic, who
dedicated so much of his energy to awakening Germany's interest in other composers, was not thinking tonight of himself—of his slowly developing career. Tonight he was thinking
of her. For him it was a night of decision.

NINETEEN

Schumann's moment of decision filled him with torment. His was a gentle spirit, one of compassion, and he could not endure the thought of bringing grief to any living thing. For a moment, almost as brief as the candle's flame, a passion had consumed him. One picture was in his heart, one dream. To the exclusion of all else except his music, his mind had clung to the vision of Ernestine. But now, with the passage of time, and though he was already seriously committed, reality was etching away at the picture, and guilt and pain intermingled freely in his heart.

How does one explain such a phenomenon? How does one say to a sweet and blameless girl those tragic words: Yes, I loved you *then*. And believe me, I would love you still—*if I could.*

What is love? In long, solitary, nocturnal walks Schumann addressed the age-old question to himself, to the silent stars. Philosophical arguments came leaping to his defense. All living things undergo change. Nothing that exists ever remains the same. Man, like the seedling, must take root and grow, nourish from the food of his experiences, and, at the peak of maturity, flower in the brightness of time.

For him, as for everyone else, there must be a time of testing. Youth's insatiable appetite for the joys of life had brought him blindly to the beauty of Ernestine; but manhood with its more genuine emotions forbade him the folly of permanent union. Here was the paradox, he told himself. Love is both a beginning and an end. To achieve it one must first reach maturity, but in order to reach maturity, one first had to endure the test of love. Thus did hearts break, and thus did one come face to face with self.

There were times when he placed the question differently. Had not the final blow really come when Baron von Fricken made that startling revelation about his "daughter?" Had not his love already undergone irreparable damage by the time Ernestine returned that next day, her blue eyes soft with expectancy, whispering in happiness, "When, Robert? When will it be?"

By then he knew that his feelings for her had been transitory, that a union based upon unequal love and further complicated by the struggles that must ensue because of insufficient income could only bring tragedy for them both; yet he feared to see the light of joy go out of her eyes. He played the coward, bitterly afraid to face her with the truth. The baron had allowed them the freedom of long walks together and he could not bring himself to deny her the promise she expected of him. When he left Asch, their exchange of rings had become formal.

But spiritually he left the baron's house a changed man. Heavy of heart, plagued with bitter regret, he made an acceptable excuse for not being able to give a definite commitment as to the wedding date, and returned to Leipzig to plunge himself deep into his business affairs and his heavy program of composing.

Carnaval was completed. After some minor revisions, he prepared his *Sonata in F sharp minor* for presentation to the publisher, and began feverishly to work on a new sonata, this one in G minor. *Carnaval*, which he described as "Little Scenes on Four Notes," was a series of short piano pieces built on the letters A*S*C*H, which said clearly enough that it was meant for his betrothed. But the sonatas? He could no longer dedicate to Ernestine this music pouring from his heart.

How? How could he tell her? If the girl had been a coquette—one of those deceiving little creatures— Oh, but there were a hundred if's. He paced his room at night calling on the speechless walls to tell him what to do. Now no philosophical answers came to ease his conscience. He blamed Ernestine for not having told him the truth about her status in the baron's household, but he blamed himself more for having been so deeply and blindly drawn into an affair from which he longed now only to escape. Aloud he uttered some bitter truths:

She must suffer so that you may survive, Robert Schumann.

For the sake of your art, you cannot, out of pity, waste yourself on this soulless girl.

Soulless? Yes! Remember her letters. How dull! How boring! All her foolish little words put into wrong order with the wrong spelling. In Henriette's garden, her sighing silences had been easier to bear.

Be thankful, as much as it may hurt the girl, that you did not discover the truth too late!

But equally bitter was his cry, "What kind of a man will I be if I abandon her now? I, Robert Schumann—"

> Be void of feeling
> A heart too quickly stirred
> Is a sad possession upon this changing earth.

How Goethe, too, must have suffered to have been able to know so well. He could not close his eyes. His room was full of whispers.

"You would forgive me all my faults, would you not, Robert, if I were *truly* the baron's daughter—if I had a dowry?"

His accuser burnt her words into his hearing. He saw clearly the misery of those tearful eyes, and he too wept in the darkness.

"It is too late," he cried out to her relentless ghost. "No matter what the cause, Ernestine, it is too late. Accuse me, as I accuse myself, but there is no turning back now for either of us. Neither you, nor I can say exactly how it happened. Yet we know, don't we, that another is standing here between us— someone very dear to us both? Have pity on me, Ernestine. Have pity! You knew it even before I. *I am in love with Clara.*"

PART THREE

TRIAL AND FULFILLMENT

TWENTY

"I WAS BORN at Leipzig, September 13, 1819 in the house *Zurhohen Lilie* in the new Neumarkt (to which my parents had moved at Easter 1818) and received the name Clara Josephine. . . ."

It was in these words that Wieck had opened Clara's diary, when she was still too young to write for herself. And he had added so that neither he nor the child should ever forget:

At Easter 1821 my parents moved to a house in the *Salzgässchen,* and it was here that I was fated to lose my mother. She left my father on May 12, 1824 and went to Plauen to get a divorce.

Through all the years of her growing up, those last words, so fraught with drama, did indeed continue to haunt Clara. She could not look at the little book without the words "she left my father" piercing her to the heart. It was a secret pain, hidden under the gloss of acquired poise which carried her so elegantly from salon to concert hall. And there were innumerable times, when her eye caught the tragic little sentence, that she would add, somewhat resentfully, "She left me, too." But this only served to heighten her love for that faraway image, whose world, as she knew, was also the world of music.

In public, at her father's insistence, Clara, from the beginning, had called Clementine "mother." But the word came off her tongue only in obedience; for to Clara, with a child's natural longing for that which is its very own, it was ever Marianne Bargiel of Berlin who was "mother,"—Marianne, the distant, the lovely, the unobtainable. Clara ennobled her with every virtue Clementine lacked; and, especially when her stepmother seemed intolerable, she was able to find refuge in the knowledge that one day, one golden day, a northern tour might take her to Berlin—

Many times she was tempted to ask her father the reason for her mother's desertion of him. But some instinct told her it was wiser to leave the subject alone. He had a way of maintaining a stubborn silence about the details of his early life, his eyes alone hinting that the past was not altogether buried. Thus the mystery of her lost mother lingered always in the background of a sometimes lonely child, and, of late, loomed larger than ever. For Clara was in desperate need of knowledge to solve a new and painful crisis of her own—the crisis of love.

She was not alone in wondering about the early life of her father. Few among his associates knew much more about him than that he had originally come from Pretsch, a small village typical of most rural communities in Saxony. Some, especially those of the Gewandhaus musicians whose memories took them back to the time of Wieck's first appearance in Leipzig, remembered him as a lean, crafty-browed young man, dressed in a black suit with high neckcloth, which gave him the appearance of a severe pedant. Oddly enough it was Police Superintendent Streubel who had brought him around to the Gewandhaus that day and made the introductions. He told them that the newcomer, then twenty-nine years old, and an extremely capable man on the clavier, was thinking of setting up shop as a piano teacher in Leipzig and desired to make the acquaintance of fellow musicians.

Wieck had a proud look and did not seem too amiable. Indeed, the old-timers at the Gewandhaus thought there was something vaguely offensive in his self-assured manner. Nevertheless he succeeded in making an impression. Wieck was one of those people whose self-confidence is of such a frankly open character that it takes one off guard and makes the granting of favors seem a matter of course.

"As I am now the most qualified pianoforte teacher in Leipzig," his look seemed to say, "it stands to reason that you will send all prospective pupils to me. . . ." He did not come like a beggar but like a king.

As articulate as he was with his opinions on pedagogy, it was soon discovered that he instantly lost his tongue if any one of his new acquaintances became more familiar than he deemed necessary. He became silent whenever personal questions arose and would throw his inquirer a look that would frighten the boldest man. One had to be cautious with this quick-tempered, ambitious friend of Streubel's. It was difficult to evaluate him accurately. Was he merchant or artist? On the one hand, his self-confident, authoritative air, his quickness to grasp and utilize every opportunity which would send him a rung higher in his profession, seemed to indicate a purely mercenary interest in music. Yet, under the heavy brows his singularly pale blue eyes revealed the most startling sensitivity. Merchant or artist, one opinion shared by all in those early days persisted through the years: it might not be easy to like this dynamic, brilliant man, but it was far wiser to be his friend than his enemy.

In Dresden, too, there were some who had had an early glimpse of him. This was only a short time before he had set out to make his fortune in *die Tante* (as musical Leipzig was familiarly called). And the setting was quite a different one: a bright Sunday morning, shafts of sunlight piercing

through the stained-glass windows of the Lutheran Church.
In the pulpit, preaching his neophyte sermon, stood a tall
lean youth, with stern, indrawn cheeks and penetrating, almost
frightening eyes. The spellbound congregation was highly
pleased with their new pastor, Friedrich Wieck, who had
only recently graduated from Theological College of Wittenberg University. But on subsequent Sundays, to its disappointment, the new preacher failed to put in an appearance. What
had become of him? Some said that, immediately after de-
livering his first (and only) sermon, he had gone off in the
company of one Adolf Bargiel to the estate of a wealthy
personage, where the two young men now served as tutors to
the man's heirs. It was rumored that, on stepping down from
the pulpit that memorable Sunday, Wieck had said, "I'm off.
Preaching goes against my conscience."

One had to journey farther back to find a clue to this
enigma. On the day that news of the flight of Dresden's minister reached the village of Pretch, a certain pastor's daughter
there, dry-eyed in her disappointment, sat with folded hands
staring out into the fields. Long ago she might have known
this day would come. Of all her children, this one, Friedrich,
had the quickest mind, an appetite for learning that was
seldom satisfied. In the midst of her impoverished life, he
was her single hope, her joy. Her husband, an obscure trades-
man struggling to overcome his numerous business failures,
gave little time to the boy. But she—she would take this
seedling and make something of value out of him.

She envisioned the ministry and saved her pennies for the
day when she would be able to send him to the University of
Wittenberg. And pennies they were, for poverty constantly
haunted the family. She saw that he had a predilection for
music and this pleased her, for she thought it no contradiction
to a career in the church. It did not disturb her if, instead of

staying home, he haunted the doorstep of such important personages as the town violinist or the church organist. The clever boy was able to pry lessons from these men, with not a penny out of her pocket. And from the distinguished Herr Milchmayer, too, who had been hired by a prosperous citizen to give piano lessons to his children, Friedrich had six free lessons! Enough. Henceforth, the boy said, he could instruct himself. Night and day he nursed the old table clavier which his mother managed to find for him. It was astonishing to hear what he could accomplish all by himself. But one day he startled her with this announcement:

"Mama, the church will not be my career after all. Like Herr Milchmayer, I will become a teacher."

A teacher! She hastened to tell him that teachers were little more than servants in the rich man's house. The ministry at least was respected. No! She would hear of nothing else.

The boy held his peace, but when he was of age to go off to the university, he took the clavier with him. Yes, a clever one, her boy. And now he had taken his education and set off to do with it exactly as he pleased. When he was just a little lad of three or four, he had a way of looking at her as if to say: "Never mind telling me what to do. I know better than you." So! Perhaps he did.

The pastor's daughter sighed and gave up her dream.

It was at Wittenberg that Streubel (later Leipzig's police superintendent) met Wieck as a fellow student. He had viewed with awe the intellectually solemn lad from Pretsch who, with greatest self-confidence devoted half his time to his theological studies, the other half to the clavier, and still managed to graduate with honors after three years.

That such a promising fellow, highly recommended by the university, should appear in Leipzig one day with an empty pocket, minus a post, and asking for a loan to set himself up in business, was a puzzle. Always the proud one, Wieck would offer little more information than that he had been tutoring lately at a private estate and wanted now to be free and independent. He wanted to put into practice some theories he had on "Instructing the Young." He showed Streubel a treatise he had written recently on the subject. The sum of it, as Streubel read, was as follows:

One must not merely drill the pupil. One must take pleasure in one's calling, cultivate an animated manner, and have the power of interesting the pupil in his work. *My principle is: teach a talented child anything he can understand that attracts him if it is likely to be useful in contributing to his development. Do not be overanxious about his age.*

Still in awe of his former classmate, Streubel gave him the loan. Intuition told him Wieck was a good risk. His only doubt was whether this fiery, determined friend of his would ever find a pupil ambitious enough to satisfy his intense, perfectionist demands.

Shortly thereafter Wieck set out on a pilgrimage to Vienna. On his return, it was rumored that while there he had made the acquaintance of the great Ludwig van Beethoven, and spent three hours chatting with him in his rooms. Such intimate association with the idol of all musicians established for the shrewd young man an enviable reputation in Leipzig. With the aid of Streubel's loan, he soon "set up shop." Many a student coming by to borrow books from his music lending-library would stay to listen to his account of his talk with Vienna's great man. Wieck did not tell them that, in order to gain admittance to the deaf composer, he had pretended to have knowledge of a new hearing device. His story, as it stood, gained him his following, and some interesting pupils besides.

Among the latter was a young girl by the name of Marianne,

daughter of Cantor Tromlitz of Plauen. Streubel soon observed that to Wieck this girl represented an unpolished jewel through whom he aspired to make his reputation as a music master in Germany. He was devoting endless hours not only to training her fingers on the piano, but to teaching her how to use properly her sweet, fresh soprano voice. It was Wieck's boast that before long he would be able to present his star pupil to the public. And he did indeed, but as his bride. In May of 1816 Streubel was a witness to the marriage ceremony of Friedrich Wieck, aged thirty, and Marianne Tromlitz, just turned nineteen. And less than a year later he was present at another impressive event: Marianne made her debut as soloist in Mozart's *Requiem* at the Gewandhaus, while the husband-teacher, beaming with pride, looked on.

Lucky man, Streubel thought. He is not an easy fellow to get along with, but he manages, somehow, to reap the best of everything. Marianne was a vivacious, good-natured girl, and intelligent, too. Under Wieck's stern tutelage, she displayed remarkable virtuosity. One concert followed another. Even when far advanced in pregnancy, she would appear in public. She also assisted Wieck in teaching, helped him tend his library, and kept the records of a new project—Wieck was now an agent for the sale of pianos. In more ways than one he had prospered. Streubel's hunch about his loan was justified. Wieck soon repaid him with interest.

Marianne's first child, Adelheid, died in infancy. Thus when the second, to whom her husband gave the name Clara, was put into Marianne's arms, she turned upon it an intense, protective love. No longer was she willing to devote long hours to practice and performing. She objected to leaving her baby in the hands of a nurse day in and day out. She and Wieck quarreled over the subject. But in the end, as usual, he had his way. Under his firm pressure (for he was ever

more ambitious for his talented young wife) she continued
to make her many public appearances. But any observant
eye could see that Wieck's little kingdom was tottering. By
the time Alwin, Gustav, and then Viktor were born, their
mother had lost her docile look. A proud spirit of rebellion
burned in her intelligent eyes. She was gathering her courage
to break free from the bondage of an ambition-mad, domineer-
ing husband.

At last the day came when the desperate young mother
packed her belongings, and fled with the children to Plauen.
All Leipzig held its breath. Friedrich Wieck was not a man
to be trifled with. Whispers floated about that Marianne had
feared for her life because of his savage temper, but above all,
she feared what he might do to her precious Clara. Already
he was speaking of turning the adored child into a prodigy,
and Clara less than five years old!

Like a wounded tiger, Wieck soon began to roar his wrath
and take his vengeance. He demanded the full right under
Saxon law to punish the runaway mother by taking her
children away from her. Marianne's pleas and tears were of
no avail. The Leipzig court sanctioned the divorce, and
ordered her to return Clara, Alwin and Gustav to her husband.
Viktor alone they left to her, because of his tender age. Grief-
stricken, Marianne returned to Plauen. A year later word
came that she had married again, this time, oddly enough, a
former friend of Wieck's, that same Adolf Bargiel who had
been his fellow-tutor following the Dresden episode. The
Bargiels soon appeared in Leipzig, and it was only after it
became painfully clear to Marianne that her three children
were lost to her forever that she and her new husband, also
a piano teacher, went to Berlin to live. It was there that the
baby, Viktor, died.

Wieck now lived with but one ambition—to show Marianne that he could accomplish with another what he had failed to accomplish with her. He began to focus his life on Clara, who was young, and pliable, and his alone now, with no dissenting voice to challenge him. To meet his new task, he summoned not only all the pedagogical skill at his command, but something else besides—a possessive, almost desperate love for his little girl, who, because she had been left too long in the care of a mute nurse, was afflicted with a speech and hearing handicap. Before he would be able to teach her fingers adequately, he must first teach her to talk and to hear!

But he was determined to overcome every difficulty. Loving him, obeying him, this little Clara would one day rise to those musical heights which her foolish mother had chosen to refuse. *Nothing*, he told himself, *nothing on earth would ever come between this child and her destiny.*

Such was Wieck's story. And Clara, now turned sixteen, had thus far never been a disappointment. But yesterday someone waited for her on the stair—last night someone called her name, and how quickly she had run to answer the call! Peering through the darkness, Wieck clenched his fist as he recognized his rival.

A force stronger than music was threatening to pull his Clara away from him. Once again Leipzig had cause to hold its breath. Once again the tiger was preparing to roar. . . .

TWENTY-ONE

DECEMBER, 1835. Fresh snow blew down from the southern hills. Bells in their cavernous hollows sang out the season. Never, Clara thought, had Christmas seemed more glorious. Was it not a miracle that all that had appeared so ordinary to her only a month before—the sights, the sounds, the faces of Leipzig—now sparkled and sang and glowed?

She was alive, and in love. She was young and she was happy. Every morning when she opened her eyes she could say with her first breath, "I'm his! I'm the most fortunate girl in the world," and then smile with her secret knowledge.

It was that time of the year when sleighing parties, ice skating and other such social activities drew hundreds of young people away from their study routines, out into the crisp delights of Leipzig winter. Now, more than ever, Clara was anxious to join in. She was up early, coaxing her brothers to hurry, and sending Alwin off with a message urging Schumann to meet them at the pond on time.

"What's come over her?" Gustav wanted to know of Alwin.

And Alwin, with his usual wise air, nudged his brother. "You don't know? Duncehead! Open your eyes!"

Only to Alwin had Clara made the wonderful confession. Though Schumann had urged her to say nothing of their new relationship to anyone until he had first told Ernestine, she had been unable to keep such happiness to herself. Her brother, who was nearly as skilled on the violin as she was on the piano, was her closest companion among the young people at home. His serious, thoughtful nature, his undiminished admiration for her and for Schumann created an unusual bond between them. No one else except Alwin could have understood so well her confession that morning in late November. "Everything is all right now, Alwin," she had told him, smiling with happiness. "Last night, I was lighting Robert's way down the stair, when suddenly—"

She had not had to explain further. Alwin had grinned with understanding. "Well, I'm glad!" he exclaimed enthusiastically. "You two—I always wanted it to happen."

Having now her heart's desire, Clara quickly lost that look of introspection which so often accompanies a young girl suffering unrequited love. All that was outgoing, sturdy and strong in her nature came to the fore. Her energy seemed boundless, her cheeks glowed with health. As she skated hand in hand with Schumann, wisps of dark hair escaping to the wind from under her little red cap, she presented less the picture of a delicate, sensitive artist than that of a typical fun-loving girl in her teens who blends well with any outdoor scene. Some of Wieck's neighbors who had seen her on the ice came in to tell him that they had never seen her looking prettier—or happier.

Schumann, too, was responding well. For the first time in months he felt a sense of physical and mental well-being. Caught up by his partner's youth and cheerfulness, he took great delight in capering like a schoolboy on the pond.

"We are right together!" he sang into Clara's ear, the wind almost drowning out his voice.

She laughed as she swung off with Alwin, and he stood by on his skates following her every motion with adoring eyes. Clara! Clara! He wanted to shout her name aloud to the winds. From the beginning life must have been planning

for them this ecstasy. Oh, where was the darkness that could
overcome him now—where the dark angel? His head literally
overflowed with songs.

Like all young lovers, they enjoyed their clandestine moments. He came to her home at every opportunity and kissed
her when he thought no one would see. Their secretiveness
wore the usual innocence of love's green beginnings, but Clara
was looking forward to the time when she would be free
to tell her father.

"I know it will please him," she said with a smile one afternoon. Schumann had just presented her with a lovely, but
expensive, string of pearls for Christmas. "Oh, Robert, we've
so much to be thankful for. If only it weren't for hurting
poor Ernestine!"

This problem, unresolved, seemed the only threat to their
happiness. Though Schumann had intended writing to Ernestine early in December, he could not bring himself to do
it until after the holidays. Every time Clara referred to it,
a needle of pain pricked at his conscience.

"She has an understanding heart. She will forgive us," he
said in a low voice. "Try not to think of it now, Clärchen—
not now."

"No," she said quickly, smiling at the furrows which had
gathered on his forehead. Sometimes Robert seemed to her
quite childlike. "Today I shan't worry about anything. And
neither shall you, sweet Robert—"

The smile revived him at once. He took her hands inside
his own. "I'm lucky in you, Clara! Heaven knows what might
have become of me—and you too—if I had not realized it in
time. Do you like to vision us as we will be later on—two
dedicated musicians busy as bees all the day, I at my composing, you at your practicing? Think what an exciting life we

can make of it. Then, in the afternoons, when we're done with our work, we will sit out in the garden enjoying the company of our children."

She laughed, for most probably their life would not be as simple as all that. "Shall I never go on tour?" she teased him.

"Now and then, but only for pleasure, my darling. I certainly don't intend to have you traveling about as often as you do now."

"I see!" Her dark eyes shone with mischief. "You will compose, I will practice, and our children, the poor dears, will want for food and clothes, and I for a jewel to wear in my ear. Oh, Robert, we shall be dreadfully poor, for no one will earn anything."

Clementine and her father often spoke of Schumann as impractical. Clara always denied it vehemently, but she was in a mood to tease him now.

Schumann studied her face with grave questioning. "You're not serious, Clara? You don't worry your head about such things!"

She shook her curls vigorously at him.

"Thank heaven we understand one another when it comes to that," he said, relaxing again. "Money can't be everything between two artists. We know what it means to work hard without filling our heads with extravagant dreams. No, Clärchen, we may never have the luxuries that Mendelssohn, or even David, can afford. But together, our gifts, yours and mine, can enrich us all our lives."

"Ah, but what if Father won't give me up to you. What if he should say, 'No, no, Clara Wieck belongs to the world!'?"

"Then you will answer him back very proudly, my girl, and say, 'But Clara Schumann belongs to her husband'—"

And there the conversation came to an abrupt end, for of

a sudden Clementine walked in. Neither Robert nor Clara noticed the odd smile at the corners of her mouth, the strange, knowing light in her eyes.

"What pretty pearls!" she said, examining the necklace which Schumann had fastened around Clara's neck. "Where did they come from?" She shook her head reprovingly, showing that she already knew the answer. "It's a pity to open gifts before Christmas, Clara. Your father will have something to say. Come! Don't bury yourselves in here, you two. I've been looking for you. Gustav and I have been decorating the tree all by ourselves—"

Only later was Clara to understand the meaning of this little interruption. She and Robert went willingly out to help trim the tree, with never a hint that this was to be the last peaceful Christmas she would ever spend under her father's roof.

For Wieck, the holiday held little more than gall. Since the evening of November twenty-fifth, when Clara had lingered too long on the stairway with Schumann after an informal musicale, a change had come over him. His eyes sat in his head like two cold beads. His thinning nose arched taut with hatred and displeasure. But he had thus far managed to hold his tongue, nursing in silence the white fury which was eating at his heart. On the twenty-sixth of November, he and Clara had set out on a quick tour to Zwickau, Plauen, Glauchau and Chemnitz. Seeking to confirm his terrible suspicion, he watched her carefully, observing that, for the first time in their travels together, she seemed oddly removed from him, content in some secret world of her own. An unmistakable liquid softness lay in her eyes, and her smiles came intermittently and without obvious cause. By the sixth of December they were in Zwickau. It was there in the concert hall that same night he had seen a familiar figure, leaning against a post in the shadows. It was Schumann following after Clara! No doubt of that. He could barely restrain himself from leaping off the platform to attack the interloper. How dare he hide himself? What was he up to? And a sick anger swept over him as he noticed that, from time to time, in certain of the lyric passages she played, Clara smiled, ever so slightly, as if her sweet and lingering song were meant not for the audience as a whole, but for one alone—that *secret listener*—

So! Wasn't this the day he had been dreading all these years—his reason for nurturing a nagging dislike of Schumann? Yes, now it was clear. And he found a capacity within himself for the darkest and most dangerous kind of hatred, the deep roots of which were already beginning to strangle his reason and smother all sense of decency. On his return to Leipzig, he thought of Schumann night and day with loathing, especially when he saw that Clara, like Ernestine before her, was restless and unable to settle herself for too long at anything until Schumann put in his daily appearance.

. . . Besides she has forgotten practically everything that has been taught to her with so much difficulty. She is like a green plant scorched by the sun—that is to say, by Schumann.

Thus he had written of Ernestine, not many months before, and now— Wieck choked on his bread. Now, it was Clara! He could not bear to see her eyes light up or hear her laugh when Schumann was in the house. He studied each fresh piece of evidence, preparing for the moment to swoop down upon his enemy. He had yet to catch them at anything, embracing or kissing— The very thought of Clara succumbing in this way to Schumann brought him almost to the point of violence.

"We must find a way to rid ourselves of that fool," he

muttered aloud one day to Clementine when Schumann was in the house. Until this moment he had not bared his feelings to her.

"Ah . . ." Clementine sucked in her breath, barely restraining a smile. He had not believed her when once she warned him about those two. Now, suddenly, his eyes were opened to things she had seen all along. So this was why he had been stalking through the house these past days as though someone in it were doing him a terrible injury . . . a glint of petty satisfaction altered the color of Clementine's eyes.

"Yes, I think you are right," she heard herself saying glibly. "Schumann is too free. He walks in and out as if he were already a member of the family."

"Put a stop to it. . . . I don't want him hanging about. . . . From now on, be indifferent," Wieck spluttered.

Clementine nodded. She did not fully understand all that motivated her husband, but somehow it did her simple heart good to see him critical of Clara for once. His wrath, she noticed, seemed to include the girl as well as Schumann. This was a turn of affairs indeed.

Pity, Clementine thought. She had nothing against Schumann, really. Indeed she liked him very well and always had. They were close in age, she being the older by five years. Unlike some of Wieck's other associates, Schumann treated her with more than just patronizing respect. He always showed genuine appreciation of her domestic contribution to Wieck's musical household. With him she never felt on the outside. He fully took her in, always had something to say, always had time to listen. He could as happily examine her latest piece of needlework as indulge in philosophical discussion with Wieck in the drawing room. Above all, he took her part with Clara. She had heard him, now and again, take the girl to task for some cold or disrespectful word; he seemed to consider it a weakness in Clara's character that she could not get along with her stepmother. This alone, under ordinary circumstances, was enough to make Clementine champion any cause of his. Yet now, in this most critical moment of his relationship to her family, she turned her back on him.

She would have argued it out that in doing so she was merely obeying the most natural law—the loyalty due to one's husband in such delicate matters. But in her secret heart, Clementine knew it was more than this. Did Schumann have his problems? Well, then, she also had hers. Heaven alone understood how many slights and what uncommon loneliness she had silently suffered in this marriage. Even on her honeymoon, Wieck took Clara along to give a concert. His time was devoted only to the child and it had never changed. She did not begrudge this nearly as much as his failure to check Clara's disrespectful behavior. Well, for once it would be possible to stand in opposition to the willful girl and still be on the side of the gods.

But Clementine was not without a feeling of uneasiness when, at Wieck's instigation, she succumbed to spying on her stepdaughter and reporting all that she knew to her husband. Unfortunately for her conscience later on, she was unduly provocative:

"Clara is going to the American ambassador's to spend the afternoon. No wonder she goes there so often these days—all of a sudden Schumann is a frequent visitor there too."

"Yes, they're sending little love notes back and forth every day, employing Alwin as messenger. I'd be ashamed if I were Clara to use that innocent boy—"

And finally the straw that broke the camel's back:

"The way they talk one would think they were already married. The other day I overheard Schumann say to her, 'Tell him,' (and they were referring to you, Friedrich) 'that *Clara Schumann belongs to her husband.*' What could he have meant by that?"

Wieck's veins stood out on his neck. Like a madman he suddenly rose from his chair and flung open the study door. Nanny, in her white cap and full black skirt, was going slowly up the stairway carrying a basket of clothes. Gesticulating wildly, Wieck shouted at her in a thundering voice, "Where is Clara?"

Frightened by the noise and the sight of her master's almost grotesque features, Nanny dropped her basket. At the same moment Alwin and Gustav came running from the practice room, where the latter had been turning pages for his brother.

"Did I ask for you? Get back to your work!" their father hissed at them furiously.

Gustav drew back at once, but Alwin was bolder. "Is something wrong, Father?" he asked in his serious way.

"You! You keep out of it, do you hear?" Wieck said, shaking a finger at him. "Who asked you to poke into things that don't concern you? I'll tend to you later, you and your note carrying." His voice suddenly boomed out again. "Clara! Come down here."

"*Nein, nein, Liebchen.* . . ." Nanny rushed up to Clara who was already at the top of the stairs. "Don't go to him. Look! Dear Lord, have mercy, he'll murder someone. . . ."

Clara gently pushed her nurse aside and came down rapidly. When had she ever had anything to fear from her father? But seeing Alwin's sensitive young face, his helpless look as he stood with his violin dangling from his arm, she assumed that it was he who was in trouble.

"Go inside, quickly," she said to him in a low voice as she passed. "I'll calm Father down."

With his jaw thrust forward, Wieck gestured her toward his study. "Inside . . . inside. . . ." He became nearly apoplectic when he saw that she was wearing Schumann's pearls.

Puzzled and frowning, Clara obeyed. She discovered Clementine in the room, unusually pale, leaning as if for support against the desk.

"What is it?" she asked her stepmother, who had not reckoned on such a savage display of temper from her husband. "What on earth has Alwin done?"

"Never mind Alwin!" Wieck said thickly, closing the study door behind him. "It's *you*, ungrateful girl."

His words were like an exploding bomb to Clara. She could not believe what she saw or heard. Never before had he looked at her so—never raised his voice. "Me?" she asked, looking in confusion from one to the other of her parents. "But, Father, I don't understand—"

"She doesn't understand," he mocked her sarcastically to Clementine. "She thinks we are dunderheads here, who don't know what goes on under our own roof."

Clara felt as if he had struck her a blow across the face. She was hurt and humiliated at his having used this tone against her to her stepmother. They had like pride, she and her father. Her cheeks began to flame. "I haven't the least idea what this is all about," she said stiffening. But there was a quaver in her voice.

Clementine, on the other hand, seemed suddenly to regain her composure. She walked with an authoritative little step to stand beside her husband. "Your innocent air doesn't fool us, Clara. Everybody knows, everybody sees your disgraceful behavior. A girl like you, with your upbringing, accepting pearls from a man already engaged to another, meeting him in out-of-the-way places, sending love notes back and forth. You put your father and me to shame."

So that was it. This little speech illuminated everything for Clara. But her father's lack of faith in her wounded her deeply. Only this morning a letter had come to Schumann from Ernestine, warm and understanding, releasing him at once from all obligations to her. And this was the very night she and Schumann had planned to confide their love to her parents. . . . "Let me explain—" she began.

"What will you explain?" her father interrupted angrily. "How, after a lifetime spent to make something of you, you lie and cheat and deceive me behind my back? But what is a father, after all," he sneered, "when you now have a brain like Schumann's to advise you? So! 'Clara Schumann belongs to her husband,' does she? Is that it, already?" His voice rose again to thundering proportions. "That idiot lifts his little finger, and without a word to me you run to give yourself away to him. For what? Love? Bah! He practices it on one woman after another . . . !"

With a flourish of his hand Wieck knocked one of Clementine's precious Dresden jars onto the floor, kicking at the broken pieces, grinding them beneath his shoes. "Let your 'Robert' come pussyfooting around here again and I'll . . . I'll *kill* him, do you hear?"

"For heaven's sake, Father, have you gone out of your mind?" Clara stared at him in horror. The unexpectedness of the attack, the injustice, the incredibility of his behavior, she could not believe it even now. "Why, Robert Schumann has lived in our house, honored you as his teacher, been almost a son to you. How can you say such outrageous things? And you!" she cried, turning to Clementine, her eyes glistening with angry tears. "How dare you speak of shame to me, you who eavesdrop on private conversations, open private letters, spy on your own child . . . oh, I take that back. I'm no child of yours, thank heaven. I see what you've done. It's *you*, with your tales, who turned Father against Robert and me."

With a proud fling of her head, she faced her father again. "Send her away, Father," she insisted. "I won't say another word while she remains in this room."

"See how she speaks to me," Clementine said defensively. "Just because she is Clara Wieck, she thinks she has the right. It's no wonder such a girl falls into trouble."

"Leave us alone!" Clara's voice rang out sharply. There was a look in her eyes strongly reminiscent of Wieck when he made a command and expected to be obeyed.

For a moment Clementine looked steadily back at her enraged stepdaughter as if she might match Clara's splendid anger. But the moment was short-lived, especially as no word of support came from her husband. He did not, as she had expected, say to her, "Stay." But then, it had never deeply concerned him, Clara's insubordination to her. "Very well," she said, going toward the door. "But remember this, Clara. It's not just idle superstition when people say, 'Pearls mean tears.' Those beads you are wearing won't bring you happiness. Ernestine, whom you betrayed, isn't the first girl to cry because of Schumann, and you, my dear, won't be the last. When your turn comes, *as it most certainly will*, just keep in mind who told you so."

TWENTY-TWO

"CLARA is stubborn. She insists she won't come in to break-fast."

"Never mind. Leave her alone. When she's hungry, she'll eat."

A silence settled over the table as Clementine took her place and solemnly unfolded her napkin. The two boys and their sister, Cäcilia, could not look at their parents. The brief dialogue took away their appetites. They could digest neither their food nor the reality of the blight which had suddenly crept over their house. Yet all were vaguely aware that some-thing ugly and corrosive had begun its destructive process, starkly dramatized by Clara's empty chair. Would anything ever be the same again? Could that which was lost in the violence of yesterday's anger ever be fully restored?

Upstairs in her room Clara was wondering the same. In time, when her father thought things over, he might regret all the terrible things he had said and done; but could time ever succeed in wiping out the memory of it, or restore to her her sadly shattered illusions?

For a girl like Clara who, from early childhood, had been used to pampered treatment, not only at home, but in public as well, nothing is more devastating than sudden disfavor. Exhausted by emotion and tears, she did not know how to cope with this new pain (than which there is none greater), rejection and denunciation from one who in the past gave only love and praise.

Throughout the senseless quarrel her father had remained cruel, cold and unmoved. Neither smiles nor tears could win him over. Had she cried out, "But, Father! You're talking to *me*, Clara Wieck!" he would have replied, "So! And who is that?"

For days she kept to her room, admitting only Nanny. Alwin dared not come. He was being watched with the greatest care lest he act as messenger again between his sister and Schumann. Visitors coming to seek her out were told that she was ill and could see no one. Twice Schumann came and twice was turned away. "We are not receiving company," Clementine told him coldly, barring the door. Clara had seen him from her window making a slow, puzzled retreat. No explanation had been given him, just blunt, cruel rejection. Finally, frantic with anxiety, he sent his new roommate, Ulex, with a message. On recognizing Ulex, her father shouted furiously from an upstairs window, "Warn your Herr Schumann to stay clear of this place, do you hear?" And poor Ulex, frightened by the leering face above him, took to his heels.

On another day it was Emilie List, daughter of the American ambassador, who came. She and Clara had been confirmed together. She, too, was treated with icy coldness by Wieck, for he suspected her of having been the culprit who had furnished Clara and Schumann with their lovers' hideaway. Since it was only during these brief periods between concerts and tours that Clara had time to enjoy the companionship of girls of her own age, she bitterly resented this treatment of her friend. Was no one, then, to be left to her? Was everyone she loved to be turned away by her father? There were many things about this dreadful business she found it hard to understand.

Thus, for Clara, the idyllic days of the past were over. At the age of sixteen, her native land looked upon her as a distinguished artist, and a celebrity. She was honored. She was envied. But at home, it now became too painfully clear, she was to be more her father's prisoner than his daughter.

Recuperating slowly from the shock, she gradually took up her daily routine again, but her heart was no longer in her work. The light had died out of her eyes. She was listless and without spirit. The hunger within her for the sight of Schumann's face, the sound of his voice, was so great that she was often tempted to risk anything to be with him. But the eyes of her parents were everywhere. Neither she nor Alwin could escape.

One morning her father told her that he was planning to take her to Dresden. She needed a change, he said, and Sophie Kaskel, who would be their hostess in the capital, always gave them a good time. However, it could not be all play; he had scheduled two concerts, one in the latter part of January, the other for mid-February. Clara's heart sank. Two long months away from Leipzig! With never a chance even to catch a glimpse of Schumann! The very idea was torture.

"No. I'm not prepared to play, Father," she said, sulking. "How can you expect me to carry through concerts feeling as I do? I'd rather remain here in Leipzig. For my sake, please, cancel the concerts—"

He looked at her almost in disgust. It was unheard-of for an artist to cancel a concert. To do so could mean ruin. "Where is your pride?" he stormed at her. "Keep up this nonsense and you'll never play another note. Do you think I've spent all these years on you for nothing? I've heard enough! Go instruct Nanny to pack your clothes at once!"

Further argument proved useless. The following morning, the fourteenth of January, as a freezing wind pummeled mercilessly at their coach windows, they set out on the long, dreary journey.

Dresden, on the river Elbe, was divided into two parts, the old town and the new. The history of the old town went back to the time of Henry the Illustrious, who had chosen it for his capital. Nested among cathedrals and ancient Gothic structures, its imperial court dominated the way of life, clinging to all the old traditions rather than following the new. Originally, Dresden had been a Slavic settlement until the Margrave of Neissen brought in the Germans. Now, as Saxony's famous capital, it was not only the residence of kings, but boasted itself a center of the arts as well.

During these past years, the Wiecks had made many acquaintances there, both in musical circles and at court. Almost as soon, then, as they were settled under the roof of their hostess, Sophie Kaskel, they were caught in a busy social whirl. Surrounded as she was by cheerful friends in the stimulating atmosphere of Sophie's salon, it was difficult for Clara to retain for long her sulky mood. But the pain of her recent experience had left its mark.

"Those eyes of hers are like two rain-filled pools," Sophie remarked one day to Wieck's close friend, Karl Reissiger, the noted composer and conductor. On her previous visit to Dresden, Clara had stayed with the Reissigers, and he, too, at first glance, could see the change in the young artist. He asked Sophie if she knew what was troubling Clara.

"No. She and her father both have too much pride ever to confess their troubles," Sophie said thoughtfully. "Yet anyone with half an eye can see that Clara is unhappy."

Sophie was one of the few women Wieck admired. Vivacious, intelligent as well as beautiful, she had the capacity of drawing all manner of people to her side. There was never a dull moment with her, and Wieck was always at his best in her house. Her insatiable curiosity had led him once to quip that she had an "incurable tongue," but it was the only fault he could find with her.

When her visitors had been with her less than a week, Sophie gave a gala party in their honor. That night the brilliantly lit drawing room was crowded with guests—musicians, poets, court officials and their wives. Outdoors the garden was buried in snow, and the trees, touching their thorny fingers against the misted panes, wore rings of ice. But here great logs lay bristling in the fire, warming the mint-green room. Dressed in a gown of maize-gold, Sophie circulated gracefully through the room, tending the needs of her guests. She soon came upon the little circle surrounding Clara and her father. In high spirits, Wieck was entertaining the group by mimicking a series of questions that the "foolish public" always put to him about his "piano-playing daughter."

"Q. When did your daughter begin?
A. Never!
Q. How old is your daughter *really*?
A. This is written under her portrait—
Q. Do not your daughter's fingers hurt her?
A. You forget you are talking about Clara Wieck!
Q. Do you not overstrain her?
A. My Clara's appearance is the best answer to that.
Q. You must be very happy that heaven has given you such a daughter.
A. Yes. Once it was snowing, you see, and a willful snowflake fell into my arms. Behold! That was Clara—
Q. Does your daughter *like* playing?
A. Really, there must be an end to everything—even answers—"

Sophie, who laughed with the rest, suddenly noticed that Clara was not joining in. Her father's jesting did not seem to amuse her, nor did she take it in good spirit when, continuing his sport, he took out of his pocket a diary note that she had written at the age of eight or nine, a tidbit of history that he liked to carry around with him.

"Here," he said, adjusting his eyepiece, "in Clara's own words she gives the *true* answer to her success. Notice her portrait of her father:

My father, who had long hoped in vain for a change of disposition on my part, noticed again today that I am still lazy, careless, disorderly, obstinate and disobedient, and I play as badly as I study. I played Hunten's new *Variations*, Op. 26, to him so badly, without even repeating the first part of the variation, that he tore up the copy before my eyes and from today onwards, he will not give me another hour—"

Once again, with the flair he had for putting on an act, Wieck succeeded in drawing laughter. "Come, Clara!" He winked. "For the benefit of all these good friends, demonstrate what you accomplished *all by yourself*, without a father's help."

Clara smiled, but gently shook her head. Though she had a reputation for graciousness, seldom refusing to play anywhere, in this instance, apparently, she was unwilling to cooperate.

"Come!" said her father again, awkwardly embarrassed by her refusal. "Give us a demonstration."

"Forgive me—" Clara looked in appeal to the many pairs of eyes that now centered on her burning cheeks. "You must excuse me—"

Struck by the rare tremor in her voice, Sophie, always compassionate, came quickly to the rescue.

"So," she said, with a laugh, tucking her arm in Wieck's, "all those things your enemies say about you are true. You don't allow your daughter to rest, but work her fingers to the bone. Well, now! Let Clara off this once. Let her save her strength for her concert. Besides, I have the most delightful story to tell about Madame Heinfetter at the opera—"

But when she was done, and the crowd began to thin out, Sophie took Wieck aside and asked him point-blank what he thought was disturbing his lovely daughter. "She is so melancholy! I've never known her to be like this! Is she ill?"

Wieck gave a wry grimace. "My *Backfish* imagines herself in love. Do you know a cure, Sophie? Clara's swallowed too much poetry."

"But poetry, thank God, is never fatal!" Sophie laughed, and going over to Clara, embraced her. "Don't you let him talk you out of it, my dear. Fathers are boors when it comes to love. A girl has to battle them every step of the way."

Clara, who had overheard her father's remark, seethed inwardly. Did he plan to make a mockery of her and Schumann in Dresden? Oh, he was mistaken if he thought she would allow him to amuse himself at her expense. "I must be careful from now on not to wear my heart on my sleeve," she told herself. "Put on a gay front! That will throw him, and Sophie too, into confusion."

"Pay no attention to *him*," she said lightly, imitating his sardonic humor. "If only I just breathe these days, he imagines I am in love. Do you know a cure, Sophie? Father's been swallowing too much poetry." She turned in the direction of the piano. "I think I should like to play now," she said. "Will you announce me?"

"Something is definitely brewing between those two," Sophie mused, as Clara, having adjusted her sheer scarf over her shoulders, began for her hushed listeners a new Chopin

Nocturne. She looked at Wieck. He was sitting forward in his chair, one finger tapping against his knee, his eyes burning with a strange tinge of resentment. What, she wondered, was it all about?

Obviously this famous father-daughter team was at odds. Had it really to do with love? Love! The melody of the nocturne flowed now through the room. The dark-haired girl at the piano, her head tilted to one side, spoke eloquently the composer's mood of longing. A poem delicately sad was being communicated through her fingers.

"Ah," thought Sophie. "I know now Clara's trouble. Despite that bubble of humor a moment ago, there's no doubt she's in love, and that her stubborn father, for art's sake, or whatever, is opposing it. Poor girl. If I know Wieck at all, she is going to have a problem with him. I must see what I can do to help her."

But in the days that followed, it was a seemingly revived Clara who danced, and skied and joined her friends at the theater and sleighing parties. Not once did she seek to confide in Sophie. Not once did she mention Schumann's name, nor sigh, nor sit in pensive mood. She called on her strong reserve of inner strength for the laughter required to hide her true feelings. Only for one brief moment, before stepping out to greet the audience at her first concert, did her nerves give way. "Clara, by God's grace," her father recorded later in his diary, "was nervous for the first time and shed some musical tears." But this was soon forgotten in the enthusiastic reception she received. He was delighted, as well, by the favorable change he saw in her. Away from Schumann she was obviously her old self again. He decided not to tempt fate by taking her back to Leipzig too soon.

That same evening, after the concert, when Clara had gone to bed, he told Sophie of his decision to continue the tour beyond February. He would, he said, take Clara first to Lower Silesia, but his new plan required his leaving Dresden for a few days to make arrangements for a concert in Breslau.

"Meanwhile I trust her to you, Sophie. But one favor while I'm gone. Put an end to all these late parties! Clara's already getting rings under her eyes. The opera, of course, I'm agreeable to. Otherwise, please keep her at home."

How he watches over her! Sophie thought. Counts the hours she sleeps, even supervises her clothes. What a bore for a young girl, year in and year out, to have only her father for a companion. She's certainly capable of thinking and acting on her own, but he quite strangles her with his attention.

"Tell me," she said aloud, "weren't you imagining all that nonsense about 'poetry'? It seems to me Clara is as happy as the next girl. Where is this 'lovesickness' you spoke of?"

"She has gotten over it," Wieck replied smugly.

"Oh?" Sophie looked at him curiously. He was a wily old man, but he apparently had his blind spots. Clara's gay front had not fooled her for a moment. "Then it must have been of little consequence, this love of hers."

"No consequence, thank heaven."

"What was he like, her discarded lover?"

After a brief silence, Wieck opened his pursed mouth: "Bah! A fool."

"But aren't *all* lovers fools?" Sophie queried softly.

"Some better. Some worse."

"And what makes you think he won't come after her?"

Wieck smirked. "The old fox keeps a careful watch."

"You don't mean to say you have that poor child under lock and key!"

"Stay out of it, Sophie. Besides, as I said, the girl's already cured."

Sophie gave him an intense, searching look. "But, my dear friend, won't there be others?"

He dismissed the question with a wave of his hand. "Just *you* keep a sharp lookout no one comes snooping about while I'm gone."

By now his companion's curiosity was at its peak. "And who, pray, is likely to do that?"

"Who else but that fool of a Schumann?" Wieck snapped out.

"Ah!" Sophie sat back, sighing with relief. At last she had what she was after—the lover's name. She knew Schumann well. He often visited her on his brief journeys to Dresden. Musically speaking, this seemed a match arranged by the gods. What on earth could the foolish father have against it? "For such poetry even *I* might forget myself," she murmured, gently pleading Clara's cause.

"Don't joke, Sophie."

"Of course. You're right. This is no time for jokes. How long will you be away from Dresden?"

"A week to ten days at the most."

"Well, then, go and rest easy, my friend. Your Clara will be well looked after. No *unwanted person* will be allowed to interfere with her privacy."

A gleam of sly humor had crept into Sophie's cat-like, Persian gray eyes. But Wieck failed to notice. Two days later, in the best of spirits, he said good-by to Clara and went on his way alone to Breslau.

TWENTY-THREE

THE CARRIAGE went at a fast trot through the winding streets. Morning sun streamed across the turreted roofs and fell in soft pools on the banks of snow. It was the loveliest morning Clara had yet seen in Dresden. For the first time, a shaft of brightness touched her heart. As she watched a flock of pigeons, rising and falling in calculated rhythm before swooping away toward the Elbe, a sudden thrill of excitement overcame her. She caught her breath in even little tides and smiled a smile that was at last genuine.

"There now! That's better, little dove," Sophie said affectionately, patting her gloved hand. "My! How long I've been waiting to see you do that."

"Oh, Sophie! If only there weren't so much to think of. Especially deceiving Father the moment his back is turned. I ought to be firm, I know, and refuse to see Robert. Yet, I *must* see him, just this once! Just one more time."

"You must and you will, and not only 'one more time.' Don't worry about your father. The Reissigers will keep your secret. He'll never be the wiser about Schumann's little visit."

Clara sighed. Despite all that had passed, her affection for her father, her sense of loyalty to him, was as deep as ever. It hurt her to imagine what he would think of her should he learn of this betrayal.

"It puzzles me how Robert knew to come just at this time

when Father was away. No one in Dresden knew about us, not even you. Do you believe, Sophie, that two people who are far apart can communicate thoughts to one another?"

Sophie laughed. "I believe, my dear child, in love. Do you remember what I told you earlier this morning when you were hesitating to go to Schumann? A woman must never lose an opportunity to be with the man she loves. Sooner or later, when we are helpless to do anything about it, our fathers sit over tables and, without a by your leave, bargain us away into some 'convenient' marriage. It's our dowry, not our hearts that determines our fate. One thing about you, Clara, if only you just realize it. You can earn your own way in the world. Your fingers are the key to your independence. Only assert yourself, child. Say, 'This is what I want,' and go after it. Don't, for heaven's sake, let that bullheaded father of yours get away with anything."

There was much in Sophie's statement Clara would have liked to challenge, especially the characterization of her father, but the carriage now came to a stop at Reissiger's door. Snug in her black and white snow cape and boots, she stepped out. "Wait here for me, won't you, please, Sophie?" she pleaded, the inflection in her voice suggesting last-moment fright.

"Wait?" Sophie drew herself up proudly. "My dear, I'd like to see anyone send me away. For these few days your Robert is here, I intend to guard your privacy like a tigress. Hurry on now. He must be growing impatient. . . ."

Inside, Clara found not only Frau Reissiger, but the faithful Ulex, who had accompanied Schumann to Dresden. They told her that he was waiting for her in the library. More timidly than ever she would have in the past, yet with a heart that was beating wildly, Clara walked through the dim passageway and opened the familiar door. In the half-light of the paneled room, he stood looking back at her as if he did not believe she was real.

"Robert?" The name came almost involuntarily in a soft little cry from her throat. Gone now was the necessity of hiding her true feelings. She could not help herself. She burst into tears in his arms.

"*Liebchen*, Clara! Don't cry. . . ." He was all but smothering her against his shoulder. His mouth was buried in her hair. "At least we're together now. Somehow, we'll find a way out of our troubles."

Yet his voice had a moaning cadence of its own. And his eyes, too, were brimming with tears. For a time he held her, rocking her back and forth, while the closeness relieved and comforted them both. Then Clara, who was always ashamed of tears, regained her composure and pulled gently away.

"You don't look well," she said, examining his face with concern. "Have you been ill, Robert?"

He took her hand and drew her along to a small bench which stood against the north window overlooking Reissiger's back garden. There, in even stronger light, her suspicion was confirmed. His eyes gave him away. Clara read in them some overburdening sorrow. "Yes, you *are* ill," she said, forgetting her own troubled time. "You ought never to have made this journey."

"But I had to come, else I would have gone out of my mind." His voice broke. "Didn't Ulex tell you about my mother?"

"No," said Clara, shaking her head.

"She died, Clärchen, two days ago. Can you imagine what misery I went through when Theresa's message came, urging me to come at once to Zwickau for the funeral, and there, in the same post, Sophie's note suggesting I come here?"

"Sophie did that?" Clara looked at him incredulously.

"Yes. 'It's your one chance,' she said. And as you can see, I came here. . . ."

Clara could barely speak. The small measure of joy she had felt on the way to their reunion was gone. It was not alone the grief because of his mother's death. She felt a sore disappointment in her heart that the betrayal of her father had been so deliberately schemed. And now, this second betrayal. What right had she and Robert to be together while his mother, who had loved him, perhaps more than her own life, descended to her grave lacking his last gesture of farewell?

"If only I had known," she said, frowning, "I would have forbidden you to come here. Don't you see, Robert? You must go now, at once, to Zwickau. Theresa and your brother need you. What do I matter at a time like this?"

"But I need *you*, Clara," he said, searching her eyes for understanding. "My God! The loneliness, the uncertainty, the fear of never being with you again. Think how it was with me. At one blow I was losing the two beings I love most in the world, you and my mother."

But his answer failed to satisfy her. Her own sense of responsibility, young as she was, gave her a kind of inner strength which he lacked. "He is immature," her father had said that day in his study. Was it true, then? Could he not cope with realities?

"Under the circumstances, people will wonder at your coming here. How will you answer them, Robert, when they ask you why you did not attend your mother's funeral?"

"Ah, Clara, don't torture me. . . ." He pulled her to him, and they sat in brooding silence, he with his thoughts, she with hers. It was not a happy beginning.

"Well, then, what are we going to do?" she said finally. Her voice was thick with sadness. Never had she suspected love would bring so much pain.

"We have a little time before your father comes back. I'll stay another day or so. You must tell me word for word what went on in Leipzig. Do you know I haven't seen Alwin even once? It was Mendelssohn who came to tell me you had gone away."

That day, and the following, when she returned with Sophie, they locked themselves away in the library and examined over and over again their difficult situation. Clara told him only as much as she thought wise of what had happened at home, for many of her father's accusations against him had been so cruel she could not bring herself to repeat them in their full strength. Even so, Schumann was astonished by Wieck's low opinion of him.

"So? He thinks me lazy, incompetent, morally weak. What else? A drunkard, too?" He could not keep the ring of bitterness out of his voice.

Clara tried to convince him that many of their troubles were due to Clementine, but he would not take her word for that. "No, Clärchen. Clementine has always been my friend. She's a good soul, though you don't appreciate her. It's your father who is behind it all. But if he thought so ill of me, why make me welcome in your house all these years? Why let me see you?"

"It's your wanting to marry me that troubles him. For one thing, he worries that you won't be a good provider. For another, he insists you'll place your career over mine—" She did not tell him that her father also had spoken of "Schumann's many affairs with young girls and married women. . . ." Yet, secretly, this was the one statement which had bothered her from time to time.

Emotion and passion put aside, Schumann took great pains to go over with her the sources of his income, and possibilities for the future. The *Neue Zeitschrift*, by now a household word in musical circles, brought in a fair revenue. He was respected for the fine job of editing he did and wielded great influence with his paper. Slowly the sales of his compositions were increasing. In addition, *Schumann & Sons*, the book publishing business founded by his father, gave him a small income which would doubtless increase now, due to the tragic death of his mother.

"You see we will not be so badly off," he told Clara. Already he was beginning to grow more cheerful. "I'll go to Zwickau tomorrow, settle my mother's affairs, and rush back to Leipzig, where I'll ask your father for an interview. A quiet talk with him should prove there are figures as well as notes in this musical head of mine."

But though they had moments of great tenderness in their brief time together, there remained all the while an undercurrent of strain. Despite herself, Clara sometimes looked at Schumann not as she had when she was a hero-worshipping child, but measuring him for the first time against the standards of her father. Though her love was in no way diminished, yet she could not but wonder what there was about him, and the life he had led, which could bring her father to such violent opposition and cause him to make the accusations he did. Schumann seemed to sense this, and more than once tormented both himself and her by testing how far those base charges against him had succeeded in tainting her love. He almost spoiled their parting in this fashion.

"Stand up to your father, Clara, when he comes back. Don't let him frighten you."

"No, but Robert, I do wish you wouldn't speak so sharply of Father."

He smiled wryly. "Shouldn't you say that to *him* rather than to me—or do you believe some of that nonsense he told you? Oh, well, if it's come to that . . ."

"You know very well I don't believe it. Why do you say such things to me?"

"Never mind. I'll talk to him myself soon. You've promised yourself to me now, Clara, and he'll just have to grow used to his 'scoundrel' of a *Schwiegersohn*. . . ."

They were sitting in a far corner of the waiting room, out of hearing of other passengers, and of Sophie, against whose better judgment Clara had accompanied Schumann to the station. Clara bit her lip. There was a catch in her throat as she looked at him. Already she was dreading that inevitable clash which must come between these two she loved so dearly, her father and Schumann. Perhaps, just for a little while, it could be postponed—"

"You mustn't press Father *too* hard," she heard herself saying in a low voice. "He's in an angry mood just now. Also he has made many plans for me this coming year. He speaks of Berlin, then Vienna. We *can* be patient, can't we, Robert? After all, I'm still young . . ."

"Ah, but I am not so young. Think of that, Clara!"

All at once, alerted by the uncertainty that had come into her tone, he became panic-stricken. He looked at her closely, noticing that her eyes, under the little red hat she wore, were moist and pleading. She made a pathetic picture, this proud young girl, who on the concert stage seemed so self-assured. Obviously she was frightened at having to make a choice between quarreling constantly with her father, or giving up the only man she could ever love.

"Clara, you're not thinking of giving me up if he demands it? God help me, if you abandon me now—"

"You don't understand everything, Robert," she said, almost afraid to look at him. "You weren't there to hear all the things Father said."

"Look at me! I want to see your eyes. You love me still?"

She nodded. When had she not loved him?

"You swear it? Let me hear you say it: 'I love you, Robert Schumann'—"

"I love you, Robert Schumann . . ."

"And I swear to be firm and strong, not even my father can frighten me—"

". . . and I swear to be firm and strong— Oh, Robert, would I be here now, if I were not?"

Seeing how strongly he had moved her, he was sorry at once. "Forgive me, Clara. I don't want to hurt you. It's only that I sometimes grow afraid."

She smiled—or it served as a smile, that half-quiver of her sensitive mouth. He wanted to kiss her, but he dared not in this public place. The most he could do was hold her hand. "You make me very happy," he said passionately.

The post horn was sounding. The passengers stirred to take their seats. Clara stood by until Schumann was looking out at her from the coach window.

"Remember now, Clara. No matter what he says, or what he does, don't waver!"

"I promise."

"And keep true to me—" His voice had grown husky. His eyes burned upon her features.

"I will—" She had no time to say more, for the coach, with a cry from the postilion, jerked roughly forward, carrying Schumann out of sight.

For a long while Clara stood motionless, unable to control her mingled emotions. She could not yet face Sophie, who had been waiting so patiently for her at a distance. Nor did she know how she would ever find the courage to face the dark days that lay ahead. For it was clear to her, if not to Robert, that their love was not to be easily resolved. It would, she knew, be a long, heartbreaking time of trial before they would ever be together again.

TWENTY-FOUR

"Sir—Be notified that from this moment onward, all communication with my daughter in any form whatsoever is strictly forbidden. The privileges formerly granted to you in my household now come to an end. See, sir, that you keep your distance. If it comes to that, I shall not hesitate to strike you down—take care—"

In mute anguish, Clara stood listening to her father's voice as he crisply triggered off each cruel word in her direction. Already, after wildly rummaging one drawer after another, he had gathered up and stuffed into a box all her trinkets and letters from Schumann. Soon the small store of treasures, with the ugly note attached, would be posted and on its way to their donor.

Though Clara had prepared herself inwardly to take whatever punishment her father might inflict in his righteous anger, she could barely endure the pain now constricting her heart. It was more for him than for Schumann or herself. She did not cry aloud when he brusquely pushed her aside, and with the box secure under his arm, walked out of the room. With bent head she listened first for the sound of his footsteps descending the staircase, and then for that next inevitable sound—she trembled when it came—with all his force he slammed Sophie's door behind him.

From some mysterious source which he did not then or ever reveal, Wieck had learned during his absence of the lovers' rendezvous. On his return to Dresden he came laden with more fury than the white sheets of wind he had seen whistling in gale across the frozen Oder. Unceremoniously, he pushed his way into Sophie's house and within minutes was unleashing on her his own brand of deadly storm.

"When was Schumann in this house?" he demanded at the top of his voice.

"Never."

"Whose idea was it, yours or Clara's, to hide him away at Reissiger's?"

"I did not know that anyone was *hiding* there—"

"Where was Clara on the night she was scheduled to go to the opera?"

"Ah, but a hostess never plagues her guests with too many questions."

"Out with it, by heaven! *How many hours a day did my daughter spend with that man? . . .*"

And on and on.

At one point Sophie threw up her arms and repeated back to him, with a half-smile, his own ironic quip: "Really, there must be an end to everything—even answers." But in her heart she had begun, for the first time, to feel a measure of pity for him. Though obviously already well-informed of all that had transpired between Clara and Schumann, he was mercilessly torturing himself to hear again each painful detail. It alarmed her to see how ill he became when, to end the inquisition, she finally confessed, "Yes, yes! I sent for Schumann. I brought him here myself—" Yet he still had not had enough. He went on to the Reissigers, there to go through the same routine once more.

It was past midnight when he returned, his anger spent, his bitterness to last forever. By the light of a sputtering candle he scratched out the day's events into his diary:

Feb. 14—Reissiger's want of principle . . . his wife—during my absence Schumann and Ulex occupied the father's place. Sophie, knowing Clara to be in good hands, takes her boa and goes to the theater in Clara's stead. Sophie, the talkative, wily, becomes Sophie the silent; and on my return looks at me as if it were no business of mine. With difficulty I drag "yes" and "no" out of her . . .

Now that he was alone, the proud mask fell away. The secret grief bursting in his heart revealed itself in a series of tremors on the lids and lips. For a long while he sat with the pen half-falling from his fingers. He was betrayed on all sides. His daughter—his friends who were now his foes. And from now on, the energy he needed to carry Clara to greater triumphs would have to be wasted in petty vigilance and endless battling. Endless? Yes. Here in the privacy of this cold room, and in this dark hour, Wieck could tell himself the truth. For what was he up against but the most invincible force of all—life itself!

Two days later, dressed in stiff black brocade, Clara played her last Dresden concert with the hall "cram full and the audience clapping its hands sore." Outside of the Kaskels and the Reissigers, no one suspected the bleak misery of the young performer or dreamed what effort it cost her to smile as she was recalled again and again.

As quickly as he could thereafter, Wieck took her away from Dresden. He could not wait to see the last of that city which he felt to be smirking at him behind his back. With sour satisfaction he castigated the "stupid public, red tape and corrupt court officials." "One plays here for free tickets, for expenses, for the poor and for the police; art falls by the wayside," was his farewell comment on the capital as he proceeded through a heavy snowstorm toward Görlitz, Clara's first stopping point on the way to Breslau.

These past few days she had barely opened her mouth to him. Though her spiritless manner gave him a fright, he pretended not to notice it. He much preferred having her fight back as she had done that first time in Leipzig.

Touring in winter was not easy. The coach lumbered slowly through the continually falling snow, trying everyone's patience. When night came the passengers stepped out under the frosty sky and plodded their way to an inn for shelter and food. Early, before sunup, the post horn sounded, the sleepy travelers came out into the damp morning, and started on their way again. Such was the life of the traveling artist. Wieck kept his eye continually on Clara, spoke to her now and again, but she responded only in monosyllables. Now each whiplash of the postilion was no less severe than his own tormenting cry to himself as he studied his daughter's brooding face. "What to do? What to do?"

He knew well enough how to deal with Schumann. But what weapon did one use against one's own flesh and blood and still not lose altogether her respect and affection? Clara, Clara! Why could she not understand he did everything for her own good? Why could she not look into the future and see what would happen if he did nothing to save her? He could hardly be expected to let her end up in Schumann's kitchen washing out his shirts, *she who had fingers meant to play for kings.* . . .

He busied his brain. Somehow he must manage to turn Clara against Schumann. He often thought about the stricken look he had seen in her eyes when he carried off her precious collection of letters. He could not know all that was in her heart just then, but it had not escaped him, that look of strong feeling. It was for him, despite his violence and black temper. He told himself that he must utilize more cleverly in the future this hold he had on Clara. After so many years of close association, his influence upon her mind was as strong as tensile cord. Despite her passion for Schumann, it could not be snapped off too easily. This at least was an advantage to be cherished.

Clara meanwhile had her own thoughts keeping her constantly in a state of upheaval. She was confused and unhappy, but she secretly clung to one bit of comfort which was unknown to her father. After his disastrous raid on her room, one of the Reissiger servants had slipped into Sophie's hands a new letter from Schumann, freshly arrived. Even now as she traveled, it was secreted carefully away inside her dress. This one, she vowed, her father would never have. Come what may, she would keep it forever.

From the Coach-Office at Zwickau. Past ten at night, Feb. 13, 1836.

Dearest Clara:

My eyes are full of sleep. I have already waited two hours for the flying coach. The roads are in such a bad state that I may not get away before two o'clock. How close you seem to me, my darling, darling Clara, so close that I feel as if I could hold you. Once I could always find charming words in which to express the strength of my feelings readily; now I can no longer do so—if you did not know it, I could not tell you. Only love me well in return—will you? I exact much, for I give much.

Today has brought me many different emotions—a letter of instructions from my mother; the facts of her death. But behind all the darkness, your image always shines, and I bear everything the more easily.

I must tell you, too, that my future is now far more assured. It is true that I shall not be able to sit with my hands in my lap, and I have much to do in order to win something which you see every time you happen to pass by a looking glass—but you, too, will be glad to remain an artist, that is to say, you will wish to help carry my burden, to work with me, to share joy and sorrow with me. Write to me about this.

My first care in Leipzig will be to bring my external affairs into order; those of the soul need no further ordering; perhaps your father will not draw back his hand when I ask him for his blessing. In truth, there is much to think about and to smooth over, but meanwhile I trust in our good genius. Fate has destined us for one another; I knew that long ago, but my hope was not bold enough to tell you of it earlier, or for you to understand. I will explain more clearly later, what I have been writing to you shortly and scrappily today. And perhaps you cannot even read this— Know then, this alone, that I love you unspeakably.

The room is growing dark. Passengers are asleep near me. Outside it blusters and snows. But I will bury myself deep in a corner with head in a cushion, and think of nothing but you. Farewell, my Clara.

Your Robert.

A month passed. Like an automaton, Clara played whenever and wherever she was commanded. The brutal weather, the almost impassable roads, the grumbling of her father when things did not turn out as he expected, did nothing to improve her spirits.

Above all, there was a new theme he constantly dwelt on: From a source impossible to reveal, *he had absolute proof that Schumann, while pretending undying love for Clara Wieck, was already busy with another woman in Leipzig.*

Clara shut her ears; she often ran from the room, but like a note repeating itself, the word "false" woke her in the morning and put her to bed at night. She had no way of knowing that this was the weapon her father had finally hit upon to use against his "flesh and blood." Unfortunately for him, he went too far. There finally came a day when she could not sit at the piano without fits of violent trembling.

Recently an article written by Schumann had appeared in the *Neue Zeitschrift,* which said of her:

To appreciate her resource one must be aware that she [Clara Wieck] stands as a virtuoso at the summit of her time. Nothing is hidden from her. She has penetrated the depths in which Sebastian Bach has entrenched himself and the heights whence Beethoven stretches his giant fist; is acquainted with the modern musical endeavor that would bridge the space between these depths and heights and imparts her wisdom to us with girlish charm. . . .

Now this "virtuoso at the summit of her time" could barely play a note. Beside himself, Wieck wrote in the diary: "Clara has lost every vestige of pride and might as well give up all thought of being an artist." Reversing his gruff manner, he began to show her only the greatest tenderness, leaving off all mention of the "distasteful" subject. He even offered of his own accord to cancel the balance of the tour and take her to Baden Baden for a long rest. But Clara replied, "Please, Father, if you love me, take me home— I want to see my mother."

This pitiful little outburst startled him to his roots. He knew, without any question, that she was referring to Marianne Bargiel and not to Clementine. He said no more about it, but made ready to return to Leipzig. It was safe now, he told himself, to go there. His shafts of poison had taken effect. He surmised, and correctly, that Clara, for the first time, was genuinely doubting Schumann. When he suggested to her gently that she take up correspondence with Ernestine again, she said, "Yes. I think I owe it her, poor girl. There is much I would like to explain and also to question her about." To herself she was now saying: "Father is right. I have only known Robert the way a young child knows a man.

Even from the things Carl writes to me about him, I see that
he is neither so good nor so pure as I made him out."

By Carl, she referred to Carl Banck, who had lately struck
up an intimate correspondence with her father, never forgetting to enclose a few lines for her as well. Her father obviously approved of Carl. He even teased her about Carl's infatuation with her. If only she had been fortunate enough
to love him instead of Schumann—how much simpler everything would be. "Perhaps I can love him—if I try." By the
end of March, this had become Clara's secret vow.

Meanwhile, unaware of all these disturbances going on in
Clara's heart, Schumann, who was now in Leipzig, was beside himself with anxiety because of her. From Sophie had
come a vivid description of Wieck's return and all that had
followed. But from the day the two had left Dresden, she
said, not a word had been received by anyone of their where-
abouts.

The picture of Clara reduced to tears and trembling, she
who had enraptured Dresden by her outstanding musical performances, enraged Schumann. Though he had left Zwickau
in a tranquil mood, armed with Theresa's advice that in every
dealing with Wieck he must remain cool and dispassionate,
on reading the threat Wieck had attached to Clara's packet
of letters, his first impulse was to go after the man and have it
out. By heaven, how much insult must he take?

Yet prudence bade him be patient a time longer. Sooner
or later, he would find a way out. Only it was most unfortunate that Clara seemed to have completely lost her courage.
What had happened to that pledge she gave him to stand up
to her father and defend herself? Now God alone knew how
long they would be separated.

Sophie mentioned Breslau—he knew only one name in that
city, that of the music professor, August Kahlert. On occasion

he had had correspondence with the professor relating to articles in the *Neue Zeitschrift*. Would Wieck, on reaching Breslau, take Clara to Kahlert? If so, perhaps this was one way of getting news about her. He would take a chance. Quickly Schumann took up his pen and wrote to this near stranger:

Esteemed Sir:

Today I bring you no musical problem to decipher, but lay before you an urgent appeal to your goodheartedness, perhaps to devote a few minutes of your life as messenger between two who have been parted. In any case you will not betray their secret. Your word on that! Clara Wieck loves and is loved. You will observe it readily by her rapt air and demeanor. Permit me for the time being to omit the name of the other one. The happy pair have, even without her father's knowledge, seen each other and spoken and exchanged promises. The father, who would handle the situation with ax strokes, opposes any engagement with threats of death—has failed a thousand times to stand between them. But now he has taken her away.

The latest information comes from Dresden. There is no exact news, but I conjecture and am almost sure that they are at the moment in Breslau. Wieck will surely call upon you, and ask you to listen to Clara. Now, my special request is that you observe for me all that Clara is doing, her feelings, her life, as much as you can ascertain, directly or indirectly, keeping all this as the closest secret.

Please say nothing of my letter to the old man, Clara or anyone else. If Wieck should speak of me, his words will not perhaps be of a flattering sort. But do not let that mislead you. You may come to know him. He is a man of honor, but stubborn. Yet I can assure you that you will not find it hard to get into Clara's good graces and confidence, for she already knows that I correspond with you, and stand in relation to her rather as a lover than as a friend. She will be happy to see you and give you her attention. Your hand, my unknown friend. I have such faith in your generosity, that you will not betray me. Write soon. A heart—a life—depend on it; indeed, my own! It is for myself and none other that I ask your assistance.

Robert Schumann.

His letter dispatched, he waited anxiously for an answer. Days, weeks passed, but no word came. Had Wieck inter-cepted the letter, recognizing his handwriting? Had Kahlert played loyal to one he knew at first hand rather than to a younger man and a stranger far away? Schumann was never to know.

Each morning he rose early and bent to his many tasks. He was determined, despite his troubles, to apply himself more vigorously to all his responsibilities. Since his mother's death, he had sobered considerably, standing for the first time in years on his own two feet. He had tended while she was alive to lean upon her heavily, allowing her to manage his money, his clothes, even to take care of his debts. Now this was no longer possible, and thoughts of his future with Clara made him realize it was time to sharpen his knowledge in many areas formerly left for others to handle. He would even, if that was what was necessary to win over Wieck, try to become a good businessman.

Personal struggle tended to deepen Schumann's understand-ing, both of himself and the world about him. He did not neglect his music, rather went to it even more avidly to ex-press what he found increasingly difficult to put into words—his deep love for humanity, his compassion for all who suffered, his own great yearning for individual fulfillment. From the piano in his room there daily poured forth wave after wave of romantic lyricism fed by undercurrents of humor, folk tale and mystery. *Florestan* dictated and signed the lighter movements; *Eusebius* the dreaming, the thoughtful, the melancholy. The pianoforte sonata, Op. 11, was completed; the great *Fantasia*, Op. 17, was in process of birth.

Schumann, the man, was vivid in his music. But his music was a poem of all mankind.

Late in the evening, drained of emotion, badly in need of rest, he would leave his rooms, a lonely figure in search of company. At the Hôtel de Bavière he often found Mendelssohn, Walther von Goethe, grandson of the famed poet, and Ferdinand David, new concert master of the Gewandhaus. Music, politics were discussed and sometimes they relaxed with small talk. But a strange silence held Schumann's tongue. He became the listener, struggling to hear what was said above the strong commotion sounding within his own heart.

Solitude is the nurse of all great spirits, the mother of heroes, the companion of poets, the friend of artists.

So he himself had written. But he could not remain for long alone. On occasion he made his way to Henriette Voigt, who had ever been his understanding friend. Even there he sat staring in gloomy silence while his compassionate hostess looked on at a loss. There was nothing she could do for him. She had no influence whatsoever with her rival and his, Friedrich Wieck; nor, if truth be known, had she much heart to aid Schumann in this new affair with Clara after the recent fiasco with Ernestine. Her door was always open to him. But he must suffer through his new love alone.

April came and the first stirrings of spring. Lean, his vitality sapped by his troubles, Schumann took to walking past Clara's house every afternoon, hoping at least to catch a glimpse of Alwin, whom he had not seen for a long time. One day, to his surprise, he saw Carl Banck coming out of Wieck's gate. Carl was wearing a curious, self-satisfied sort of smile as

he thrust on his hat and turned off in the opposite direction.
Schumann rushed to catch up with him.

"Say, Banck! Where are you off to in such a hurry? Wait.
I want a word with you." Breathlessly he pulled at his friend's
sleeve.

Banck swung around with a startled expression. "Where
did you spring from?" he asked Schumann. "You gave me a
fright pulling at my sleeve like that."

They had been working together quite closely of late on
the *Neue Zeitschrift*. But for the past day or two Schumann
had seen nothing of his smooth-talking associate. He noticed
now that Banck was wearing a new suit.

"I saw you come from Wieck's house just now," he said
excitedly. "What were you doing there? Whom did you
talk to? Was there any news of Clara?"

Banck, having recovered his composure, smiled at the rush
of questions. "Come," he said, pulling Schumann along, "let's
talk over a flask of beer."

Reluctantly Schumann allowed himself to be engineered to
a nearby inn where Banck took an open-air table. It was an
extremely pleasant day. One could already feel in the air the
restless excitement of that best of all seasons. The garden,
soaked with recent rain, wore delicate tendrils of green, some
with half-open buds. Many people were out on the streets.

Banck, in an expansive mood, ordered the drinks, insisting
to Schumann that he alone would stand the cost. "No. Put
away your money," Schumann said, annoyed by something
too patronizing in his companion's tone. He pulled his own
from his pocket and laid it on the table. "Rather tell me what
news you learned just now at the Wiecks."

"Mendelssohn ought to have told you already. He was
there earlier today—" Banck picked up his glass and took a

long draught. Schumann watched him impatiently as he took time to wipe his mouth with his napkin.

"Told me what?" he asked uneasily.

"Why, that Clara has come home, of course."

"Home?" Schumann sat as if in a daze, staring at Banck without really seeing him. "Home? He's brought her home?" he repeated in a low voice. "Then what am I doing sitting here—" Yet he did not move.

"Are you all right, Schumann?" Banck leaned forward, trying to catch a spark from his friend's rather glazed eyes. "Listen! Don't worry about Clara. It gets you nowhere. She's in good health, and fine spirits, too. Mendelssohn came to her this morning, bringing a new scherzo for her to hear. Afterward we had dinner, all of us together, and sat about, talking and laughing—"

Schumann tried to take in this picture. After the torture he had been through, he could not visualize Clara "talking and laughing." "So, she is in good spirits?" he asked tonelessly.

Banck nodded. "Look here, Schumann. I'm aware, as is everyone else, what's been going on between you, Clara and the old man. But I must say Clara bears up better than you. As I was watching her today I couldn't help but say to myself: 'What a contrast between those two—Schumann barely eats, walks around with a long face, suffers every moment she is out of sight, while Clara, without a care, sits talking and smiling and putting away a good dinner. If I were Schumann, I'd forget about her—' "

"Mendelssohn too saw this? He shares that opinion?"

"You're dining with him at the Bavière tonight. Ask him yourself."

Schumann suddenly stared at Banck with a new interest. "How came *you* to be at the Wiecks today?"

"The old man sent for me first thing. He wants me to board in and take up Clara's voice training. I worked with her once before, you know, when I went touring with them last fall. . . ."

"I see." Schumann was attempting now to recall all Banck's past connections with Clara. He vaguely remembered her having said once in jest that Banck would marry her if he had half a chance.

"Did she ask after me?" he said in a low voice. A sudden fierce jealousy of his companion had taken hold of him.

"No, but then Wieck was with us the whole time—"

"And to you she didn't appear in the least depressed and unhappy?"

"Unhappy?" Banck shrugged. A half-smile appeared on his mouth as if Schumann's question were amusing. "If you don't mind my saying so, Schumann, the way you asked that is almost as if you *want* Clara to be as miserable as—"

His words were left hanging in mid-air. With a sudden violent motion, Schumann pushed over his glass and stalked away from the table. He looked in flight like a man who had just had news of losing all his wordly possessions.

Long after he was gone, Banck sat motionless in his chair, staring at the overturned glass. He was trying, without success, to remember what he had been so pleased about just before running into Schumann.

TWENTY-FIVE

A LONG, joyless summer dragged by. The two were estranged. Now there were false suspicions and wounded feelings on both sides. And when her winter tour began, Clara felt only relief. She no longer cared to remain in the same city where there were so many daily reminders of Schumann. She left with Schubert's plaintive melody silently sung within:

> Naught may'st thou ask me,
> All unspoken
> Must be my secret, ne'er revealed;
> Ah, would to thee I might but give
> A token—
> But cruel fate not so hath willed.

But there was compensation. One raw, cold morning in February of 1837, she stood with her father in the alcove doorway of a modest little house in Berlin. With a quick, decisive motion he sounded the brass knocker, and a moment later was saying to the woman who appeared, "Here, Madame, I bring you your daughter."

For a moment Marianne Bargiel stared at them in obvious disbelief. The shock was almost too much for her. She opened her mouth to speak but no sound came. To make matters worse, Wieck, who had no heart for the scene to follow, suddenly turned on his heel and disappeared as quickly as he had come, all but running down the sunless street. He

had done his duty. Now let mother and daughter get acquainted on their own.

Frantic at being so deserted, Clara's eyes sought in despair
his retreating figure. When they returned once more to Marianne they were filled with a look of intense shy agony. It was
a difficult moment for them both, but the older woman
quickly recovered and, taking Clara's hand, drew her gently
inside.

"Come," she said with a brave smile. "Let me have a good
look at you, Clara."

In the privacy of her own narrow hallway, she stood back,
almost timidly, examining the face of her daughter, the
beloved child she had lost. She did not dare, after all these
years, to do anything so bold as kiss or embrace her. "No, I
can't believe it, even yet," she murmured. "There were posters
on the Opera House, saying 'Clara Wieck Coming to Berlin'
and for days I have been asking myself, Will he bring her to
me, will he bring me my own daughter?—"

"We should have let you know. I—we—only just arrived,"
Clara stammered in hesitant apology. So many fine words
she had planned to say! How she had dreamed about them!
But here stood her mother, in this dim light, all the heartbreak
of their long separation written in her eyes, and she could say
nothing sensible or coherent. Words caught in her throat.

Marianne took from her her cloak and muff. "Forgive me,"
she said, "you must be tired, and I keep you standing here.
I know what it is to travel in such weather."

She led Clara into the parlor, gave her a seat near the fire,
and rushed back and forth, putting on water for coffee,
setting up a little table with cups and saucers, stopping now
and again to exclaim: "Clara? Is it really you?" or "What a
pity Adolf is not here—and my two boys. They will be disappointed to have missed you."

Not yet forty, Frau Bargiel retained the grace of a youthful figure. She looked much like her daughter. Both had the same dark eyes and hair. The smile, too, was the same. Watching her as she moved from one task to another, Clara noticed that her hands were strong and capable. She had the fingers of a musician, yet it was easy to see that she was skilled in household tasks as well. There was something almost luminous about her personality, yet she gave no feeling of fragility. At one glance Clara felt her to be all that she had ever dreamed. Beautiful, tender, strong, understanding.

She looked quickly around the room—this haven to which her heart had wandered many times in imagination. It too did not disappoint her. It was neither too tidy nor untidy. Books, maps and albums lay casually about. The piano with stacks of music on top dominated everything else. On the mantel, centered between pictures of two handsome boys, was a likeness of herself. No, she was not forgotten here. How happily, then, did she feast her eyes on every object within her view— Herr Bargiel's many pipes, a basket on the table containing multicolored squares and circles for a half-finished bed quilt, and a few obvious little trinkets belonging to a boy's world. A cat roamed the rooms freely, coming up to curl its graceful tail against the folds of her traveling skirt, then bounding away to its own warm place under the stove.

What, Clara thought, if I had grown up in this house, with my own favorite corner to nestle away in, living in a girl's world of dolls and sewing baskets, having that soft gray and white cat to talk to and fondle? Would I have become a virtuoso then? If not, would I have been happier for it? It was hard for her to think of herself as any other than "Wieck's daughter," as some called her, "the child wonder, the piano prodigy."

Yet she had changed greatly in the past year. Now seventeen, taller, and much more serious in her demeanor than formerly, she was aware that her eyes no longer sparkled as they had in earlier times, and that she bore herself somewhat stiffly, as one does whose pride has been badly hurt and who will never permit it to happen again. Even now she was fearful of revealing herself too quickly to her mother. There had been a time when she was capable of open, spontaneous affection, but she was more cautious now. No longer would she give her love so freely, so passionately, to anyone. She could not risk being wounded yet once again.

Marianne was conscious of this stiffening in Clara. She was even a little afraid of her. Twelve years of separation was a long time. What, if anything, had Wieck told her of the past? Did she have bitterness or resentment locked away in her young heart? Or was it that Clara's life as an artist had marred her naturalness, spoiling her for simple, everyday people. It would be a disappointment to her if the last were true, yet she suspected, from that first frightened look of shyness Clara had given her, that underneath this stiff pose there dwelt still an unsophisticated core. It had only to be brought out.

She served their coffee and, to help Clara over her silence, began to ply her with questions. How long would she be in Berlin? How were Alwin and Gustav? Had she brought any letters from them? Were they, too, studying instruments? How old was Clementine's child?

Little by little Clara's answers came more easily. There was so much to tell about home—so much she could not tell as well. But talking was far better than sitting with her tongue tied. And Marianne, whose years of teaching were revealed in her ability to draw one out, also had little ways of encouraging smiles and laughter. She opened an album, which she had been keeping through the years, of her "famous" daughter.

"See," she said, "here is a letter from you, the very first you ever sent!"

Clara had quite forgotten it, but there, in her own childish hand, were a few words to her mother, which her father had permitted her to send in 1827:

Dear Mother—You have as yet read nothing from me, but now I can write a little, I will send you a little letter which will please you. I had presents on my eighth birthday from dear Bertha and from my dear Father I got a beautiful dress and a lovely knitting bag. And I played Mozart's *E flat major Concerto* which you used to play, with orchestra accompaniment. It went very well and I never stuck at all, only my cadenza would not go easily. . . .

Plum cake and concertos! The child-artist mixing all together as if they were one slice. "Adolf and I have laughed over that many times," Marianne told her.

Next came a clipping from the *Leipziger Zeitung* of her solo debut in the Gewandhaus. What memories that brought back. "On November 8th, the eleven-year-old pianist Clara Wieck gave a concert in Leipzig. The excellent and remarkable performance of the young pianist, both in playing and in her compositions, aroused universal admiration and won her the greatest applause. . . ." Included also were copies of Schumann's *Neue Zeitschrift* with her name underlined whenever it appeared. Clara was not surprised to see them there. The paper was widely read now. But she said nothing to her mother of her special interest in that journal.

When the book was finally closed, Marianne said with a smile, "As you see, Clara, I always kept you here. . . ." Her eyes said the rest. *Long ago I had to leave you, but not once*

*in all these years did I stop dreaming of you, worrying about
you, wanting you. . . .*

Clara needed no words to understand. Her heart, too, was
very full. At that moment the last semblance of resentment
she had ever felt toward her mother for leaving her slipped
away. Whatever had happened that long time ago could
not have been through any willful fault of hers.

They read one another well. Suddenly all restraint between
them was gone. Marianne put out her arms, and Clara went
into them gladly, responding with all the true warmth of her
nature. She stood cradled against those comforting shoulders,
absorbing the love of the mother she had so missed through
the years.

"Our schedule here is very heavy," she said regretfully. "I've
eight concerts to do, besides taking theory lessons from Professor Dehn. But I'll find a way to come to you every day—
if you let me—"

"Let you?" Marianne ran her hands down the contour of
Clara's angular young face. "This is your home," she said
softly. "No matter where you go in the world, or what becomes of you, I want you to think of it that way always. Now
that I have you back, I don't intend to lose you. Tomorrow
we'll talk more and get better acquainted. There is so much
about you I still want to know."

Though she had to rise early to fit their meetings in, Clara
returned to her mother's house daily. Now, for her, there
was a kind of golden aura over everything connected with
Berlin. Her father, on the other hand, did nothing but fume
and grumble. Besides his uneasiness over her daily visits to
her mother, he was harassed, as usual, by "red tape." In
Berlin, advertisements had to pass the censor five times before
being approved. "There is no giving a grand concert here;
it would take a man half his life," he complained to the diary.

It infuriated him also that certain prominent artists refused to attend Clara's concerts. Everyone who was anyone was jealous of everyone else. He called the Prussian capital "a sink of iniquity" from which he longed to get away to "better people."

Clara meanwhile enjoyed eight gala performances, was received at court, feted by notables and acclaimed for being the first artist ever to perform Beethoven's *Appasionata Sonata* in Berlin, a city stubbornly jealous of its own traditions in culture. At each concert her mother, with Herr Bargiel, was there to applaud her. Little wonder that she played with "unequaled fire," as the critics said. But only she and Marianne knew that the flame had been lit because of certain intimate talks they had had, resulting in a rekindling of her hopes for salvaging her romance with Robert Schumann.

One morning, after spending a delightful hour playing duets together, Marianne had suddenly asked her, "Clara, do you ever give thought to your future beyond music? Do you sometimes think of getting married, for example?"

The bold question caught her off guard. Though she had longed to confide in her mother, most of their talks had been restricted to less personal matters. "The way my life goes," she said, flushing, "I'm afraid marriage is not for me."

"Not for you! What do you mean by that?"

"Simply that I've much too much to think about just preparing for concerts."

Her mother looked at her thoughtfully. "I see. So you intend to give up all other pleasures and dedicate yourself to music. Is that it?"

"I don't regret it," Clara said quickly. "Playing the piano is all that matters to me now."

"I suppose," said Marianne, "that this high-minded view of things pleases your father."

"He thinks art should be put above everything else."

"And you?"

Clara paused. "There are times when it is difficult, but the rewards are very gratifying."

"Yes," replied her mother, "but one has to live a little, too, else art dies."

After a brief silence, she asked, "Have you ever been in love?"

"Yes, once. But that's all over. It was a mistake in the first place—"

"You don't sound very convincing. Shall I tell you something, Clara? I've watched you carefully since that first day you came. I find you intelligent, sensitive, kind, but not all alive as you should be. It's as if you are holding yourself back from the light, so that no one can see your heart. I hear it, too, when you play. Something lies under the surface, rather too quiet for a young girl. And yet when I look at you I think, what a brilliant spirit! Oh, if only someone could once touch it off, what sparks would fly— Why don't you tell me about this love of yours?"

Quietly then she had told Marianne her story, softening, for her father's sake, some of the harsh details. Yet, curiously, her mother was quick to grasp and fill in the missing pieces. It was almost as if she had been through some similar experience. And there were many aspects which she questioned sharply, particularly that portion which dealt with Schumann's "duplicity." She had come to know this man, she said, through his wonderful paper. He had been a hero in her eyes long before she knew of Clara's love for him. She read sincerity, love, kindness in all that he wrote. No other critic that she knew was so impartial, so anxious to introduce new, unknown artists, or was so modest—for seldom, if ever, did he mention his own marvelous contributions to music.

Could *this* be the man her father told her was "dissolute?" Could this be the man Carl Banck assured her was "constantly unfaithful?" No, she could not believe it.

"You refer to Carl Banck as 'Robert's good friend,' " she said, frowning. "I find that disconcerting, under the circumstances. Tell me, Clara, what is this Herr Banck to you?"

"For the past year, my singing master."

"And nothing more? Is he in love with you?"

"Yes—but not I with him."

"Ah! Now it becomes clearer. And I feel quite sorry for your Robert, who cannot say a word in his own defense, while your father refuses to reveal his source of information, and this clever Herr Banck (who obviously hopes to win you for himself) tells you every kind of fanciful tale to turn you against his one and only rival. Come, Clara! Doesn't this want looking into?"

From that moment on, something definite had been struggling to come into focus in Clara's mind. Motivations. Her father's for so suddenly bringing Carl into the house. Carl for his distressing habit of dropping incendiary remarks about Schumann in front of her. Why, even on that first day when she arrived home from Breslau, he had mentioned twice having seen Schumann in company with Henriette Voigt, and said in an aside to Mendelssohn, "One never knows what he (meaning Schumann) is thinking about when it comes to women."

Could he have been deliberately provocative to gain his own ends? And if he were capable of that type of deceit, what might he not have said to Schumann about her? She shuddered to think what falsehoods could have been responsible for the bitter, accusing look she had sometimes seen in Robert's eyes when they had passed one another on the street, coldly, without speaking, during that terrible summer. How often she had lain awake at night, trembling because of it, wondering what he thought *her* to be guilty of, he who was false to so many. Why, to satisfy herself on certain points about him, she had even secretly written to Ernestine; even now it was hard to put the girl's pitiful little replies out of her mind:

July 29, 1836:

Schumann has sunk deeply in my estimation. I would have given my life for him, I could do nothing else but think of him, from each of his words his portrait looked out smiling so roguishly at me. Indeed you know his smile. O it is enchanting. . . .

And again on September 10th:

Life goes so against my grain, I wanted nothing but to be out of this world, for in it one has nothing but anxieties, torments and cares. He wrote me I should save myself while there was still time, that is the whole of it, apart from this I know of no reason, for he did not write me any and to begin by involving myself in long questions, no, that I did not do, I set him *free at once, quite free.* Schumann is entirely to blame for my present misfortune, for I feel myself wholly abandoned and miserable. . . .

How easy it had been to identify with Ernestine then, for "wholly abandoned and miserable" was her own feeling at that time.

But now her mother had awakened her out of blind, sense-less jealousy to conscious thought. She saw her own petty subjectivity, and felt ashamed of the childish manner in which she had fallen prey to the traps set for her by Carl and her father. She grew impatient to return to Leipzig to set things right again.

How endless the tour seemed! From Berlin they went on

to Hamburg, Bremen, Hannover and Brunswick, with the words, *You know his smile, O it is enchanting*, ringing in her mind all the while. Achieving artistic triumphs far beyond her expectations, she took every bow dreaming only of him, her love; but there were moments when a terrible fear overwhelmed her that perhaps he would not forgive her so easily, that she might even have lost forever her one chance for happiness. She could hardly wait to reach home again to find out.

At last, in the spring, their carriage was rolling along the streets of Leipzig again, where lime trees were blossoming in the May sunlight, where any moment she might catch a glimpse of *him*. Her heart quickened at every turn, gladness and disappointment mingling as she cast her eyes about in hope and caught the faces of many who were familiar, but not the one she sought. Carl, who had come to meet her at Lützschena, sat at her side, but she felt only the strongest repulsion for him. She did not like his eyes, nor the touch of his hand on her elbow, nor his voice speaking so possessively at her ear. Tonight, she would insist to her father that he be dismissed. First sight of him, with his oversmooth manner so contrary to Schumann's simple, warm sincerity, was all the proof she needed now as to who was "false."

But as it turned out, before she had time to speak to her father about him, Carl took the occasion of her homecoming to bring up a subject which apparently he had long had in mind; he asked for her hand in marriage. At once, on his own, her father sent him packing; Carl not only left her house, but Leipzig, too. He was outraged and humiliated by the rebuff. Why, then, had Wieck encouraged him in the first place? In his conceit, he had built up the highest hopes. And with that strange perversity of one who has no one but himself to blame for his misfortune, Carl attributed his downfall to the very man he himself had betrayed. His enmity for Schumann now became so great that he vowed, on departure, to return to Leipzig one day and "get even." Clara little dreamed then that there was to come a time when he was to be given that chance.

With Carl gone, she had no further obstacle to blur her view—not even her father. "You have your own life to live! Friedrich will just have to grow used to that." With these words her mother gave her leave. Now, she had only to contact Schumann (after all that had happened, it was certainly her place to make the first move), but how? It must be carefully thought out.

In June, not yet having found the way, she left to vacation at Maxen, the country house of Major Serre, a friend of her father's living not far from Dresden. She was glad to go, for she needed time both to recuperate from the strenuous tour and to think. She was thoroughly ashamed of that cowardly girl of the year past who had fled from love. Bolder now, she saw herself for the first time with true dignity, her mental image of Clara Wieck becoming subtly merged with that of Marianne Bargiel.

Her proud, courageous mother had come through severe troubles to the successful management of home, children and a career in music. Well, then, Clara determined, she too could do the same.

TWENTY-SIX

THE YELLOW LEAVES of the lindens were already beginning to turn in August. The drowsy heat waned and the first cool breeze brought vacationers home from the mountains. Once again, to the delight of the merchants, students were rummaging through bookstalls, cafés and shops were humming with business, and sharp trading was going on in the market place. To those who had been fortunate enough to escape into idle pleasures, the summer had been all too brief. To others, like Schumann, who alone of his circle had remained in Leipzig, it had been long and dismal. But the new season, in which Leipzig could easily rival Berlin, promised many lively events —philosophical, political and literary debates at the University, as well as stimulating projects in art and music for those who were interested. Schumann, therefore, was as glad as the shopkeepers that the town had stirred to life again.

One day toward the middle of the month, as he sat at his work desk surrounded by scrolls and pens, he saw a familiar figure coming up the walk of Frau Devrient's boarding house. The bell sounded, and a few moments later, the landlady was knocking at his door.

"A gentleman is asking to see you," said Johanna Devrient in a whisper. She was a stout, good-natured looking woman, of ruddy complexion, with blue eyes and fading yellow hair. Her kind heart prompted her to take a warm motherly interest in everyone under her roof, but Schumann, since his mother's death, had become her special favorite, whom she looked after like a son. "I don't fancy you want to be disturbed this time of the morning," she told him, "so I thought I'd—"

"No, no," Schumann interrupted her quickly. "For heaven's sake, don't send him away. He's a good friend whom I haven't seen in a long time."

Ernst Becker, Examining Magistrate in the mining office at Freiburg, a correspondent of Schumann's in that city, and an old friend of the Wiecks, did not wait for Frau Devrient to come for him. Having heard Schumann's invitation as he stood in the doorway, he rushed forward.

"I must apologize, my friend, for bursting in on you this way," he said, as soon as the landlady had left them alone. "But I'll be as brief as I can, for I quite understand how annoying it is for a composer to be disturbed—"

"It's all right, Becker," Schumann said, shaking him cordially by the hand. "You mustn't let Frau Devrient frighten you off. She's a good watchwoman, and I don't know what I'd do without her, but sometimes she gets a bit out of hand. Come, sit down. I'm eager to hear what brings you to Leipzig."

The Magistrate, a man of medium height, round-faced, with deep-set, friendly brown eyes, took a chair opposite Schumann at his desk. He was impressed by the orderliness of Schumann's rooms, so different from the public's conception of the "artist's garret." The sun streamed in. The open piano was well dusted. Books were neatly arranged on the shelves. On a small commode, barren of ornate trimmings, stood three portraits side by side. Becker recognized them as the composer's heroes—August Schumann, Jean Paul and Napoleon. Altogether it was a pleasant place of work.

"I came to Leipzig especially to see you, Schumann," said

Ernst Becker, smiling mysteriously as he put a light to his cigarette. "But you must forgive me if I behave somewhat clumsily. A case like this is a little out of my line."

"What do you mean, 'a case like this'?" Schumann asked, intrigued by his visitor's manner.

"Well, let me begin from the beginning. Early this month, I had an invitation to spend a few weeks near Dresden, vacationing with Major Serre at Maxen. I was delighted to go. The surroundings are beautiful. Also, one always meets the most interesting people at the major's. Perhaps you know that Clara Wieck, for example, spent her summer there."

Schumann instantly stiffened. His mouth pursed, and his lashes quivered perceptibly. "I know nothing about her," he said almost sullenly.

"It was she who sent me here—and just to see *you*," Becker said softly, keeping a close watch on the younger man's reactions. In his post as magistrate, he was known to be an astute judge of men, tactful and compassionate. For this reason, as well as his many-sided interests in art, literature and music, he had countless friends in all walks of life, who often came to him for help in time of trouble. He noticed now that, since their last meeting, Schumann had almost completely lost his former boyish appearance. Trouble had lined his high forehead, and the generous, sensitive mouth was grim and unsmiling.

"I don't know what she can want from me," Schumann said, feigning indifference. "I haven't heard from her for eighteen months."

"Yes, I know. To the day," said Becker, smiling. "Clara counts them, too."

"Then she does it to amuse herself," Schumann muttered stubbornly. "There's no longer anything between Clara Wieck and me."

"So I've been told. Do you know that she is playing a concert at the Börsenhalle in three days?"

"It's my business to know that," said Schumann, dodging Becker's persistent eye. Clara had not played in Leipzig for almost two years.

"Are you planning to be there, Schumann?"

"No," Schumann answered dryly. "I am not." He was beginning to wish Becker would mind his own business, or at least come to the point.

"What! Not even to hear Clara play your own *Études*?"

Schumann looked up in astonishment. "She is going to do that?" he asked, almost in a whisper. "I don't believe it. She wouldn't dare—"

"Ah! You see! You don't know *everything*," Becker said with a note of triumph. He leaned forward and flicked an ash from his cigarette. "It may interest you to know that the decision to play the *Études* was entirely Clara's alone, but Wieck agreed without a murmur. He's too fine a musician to let a personal feud affect his good sense in music."

"Yes, he's a generous man," Schumann responded bitterly. "He lets her play the compositions even of someone not good enough to shine his shoes—"

"Perhaps the passage of time has altered his feelings toward you a little," Becker argued, "though I know first-hand that he expects you to remain away from the concert. As for Clara, her greatest hope is that you will be there. It was for this that she sent me to Leipzig—to beg you, Schumann, to come."

"No! It's madness!" Schumann cried, rising and walking away. "What kind of a game does she play with me? Does she think just like that I'll let this terrible business start all over again?"

His voice trembled with agitation. His inner turbulence

was evident in his bent shoulders as he stood, with his back to Becker, looking out into the street. "Father and daughter are the same," he mumbled more bitterly than before. "First they turn me out, then throw me a crumb—no, thank you."

"You do Clara an injustice," Becker pleaded softly. "Believe me, Schumann, this is not easy for her. Think what courage it took to give me her confidence. How did she know I would not take it back to her father? And sending me to you this way! Only a brave girl could do that. She may have her faults, but Clara Wieck is no coward. A certain 'friend' slandered your character to her, and it was when she became convinced he lied—"

"Banck?" asked Schumann quickly, turning around.

Becker nodded. "She got rid of him at once; but now she's filled with remorse for having doubted you. Come to her concert, and return her letters, those her father forced her to turn over a year ago—she begs you to do these two things as a beginning. . . ."

Schumann sat down again. He covered his face with his hands. "A beginning! Good heaven! Is that what she calls it after the torment she has put me through these past months?" There followed a few moments of silence, then Schumann sighed heavily, and continued in the same bleak tone. "To you, Becker, I can say it. Next to my mother, those two, Clara and Wieck, were closest of all in the world to me. I considered myself one with them. Because they valued me, I valued myself. But something dreadful happens to a man when suddenly he finds himself despised by those he loves. He looks inward and imagines all kinds of evil." A shudder passed over him. "I don't think I can look at Clara now and feel the same as I did before. To say I 'love' her is to use too mild a word. But I'm afraid she's lived in Wieck's shadow too long. She can't separate herself from him long enough to give herself to me. In that way she's still a child and I hesitate to touch her. . . ."

Becker was deeply moved by Schumann's emotion. It seemed to him that not only Wieck, but the whole world, was overlooking this humble genius, withholding from him both a bride and the laurel of rightful recognition.

What a blow it must be to the inner dignity of such a man, who, like a single trumpet of spring, was always the first to announce with gladness all that was good and new in the music of his peers, only to have his own brilliant compositions relegated to a few "parlor" recitals and morning concerts, such as the one Clara was to give on the thirteenth. And now to be scorned by his own teacher as "not good enough" for his daughter—it was enough to crush even a less sensitive man.

The magistrate looked at his young friend compassionately. "Surely you understand," he said gently, "that this entire business was a great shock to Clara. It never entered her mind that loving you would divide her from her father; and as you say, she was tied to him hand and foot. But the experience has brought her face to face with herself. At least she's courageous enough now to battle the obstacles, even the ones within herself. Give her a chance, Schumann. Don't punish her because she faltered for a moment—"

"Punish *her?*" Schumann exclaimed incredulously. "Is that the way you see it, Becker?"

Becker nodded. "Haven't you both suffered enough? End it, Schumann. Don't refuse her just when she's anxious to make things right again. Perhaps I'm a meddling fool, but I don't want to go back to Clara and tell her your stubborn pride stands in the way. You should have seen her that night at Maxen when she was telling me her story. Her eyes filled with tears just to mention your name. What a passionate, warm-hearted girl she is! The man who has her some day can thank his stars. Will it be *you*, Schumann? All you have to do, believe me, is to ask for her."

"And if Wieck refuses—?" said Schumann, trembling.

"Well, then, eventually, you may have to take the matter to the authorities. But my own advice is that you be patient with him, Schumann. It's quite understandable how he feels. You, who know him better than I, ought to realize that for anyone to take that girl away from him is to tear into his very soul. I'm not sure that if I were in Wieck's shoes and had spent all those years developing my daughter's talent I'd behave any differently. But I repeat. Be patient with him. He may decide to lose gracefully. Love is a powerful opponent, even for Wieck."

"He'll never give her up," Schumann said in a low voice. "I *know* it, Becker. And to battle him in court would be terrible—"

"Now it is *you* who are afraid," Becker said quietly.

Schumann looked the magistrate steadily in the eye. "No, by heaven, I am not!" he said, after a moment's reflection. "And especially now that I know Clara wills it." He leaned forward and shook the older man's hand vigorously. "Thank you—thank you, dear friend."

"Well," said Becker, standing, smiling. "Shall I carry no message back to her? Where are those letters she asked for?"

"Forget those," Schumann said excitedly. "Tell Clara I will send her new ones. And you can assure her that I will be at the concert on the thirteenth. By then, you will already have handed her the first of the new letters."

Three days later, and only an hour before the opening of the Börsenhalle concert, Becker handed Clara an envelope, on the outside of which the following words were written:

After many days of silence, full of pain, hope and despair, may these lines be received with the old love. If it exists no longer, please return this letter to me unopened.

"He doubts me still," Clara said in a quivering voice. She could barely keep her fingers from trembling as she tore open the envelope.

My dearest Clara, [she read,] are you still firm and true? My belief in you is indestructible, yet the stoutest heart may become confused when nothing is heard of the being whom one loves best in the world. And you are that to me.

A thousand times I have thought it all over, and everything said to me, "It must be, if we will it and act." Write me a simple "yes" if on your birthday you will give your father a letter from me. Just now he seems well disposed toward me and will not thrust me away if you beg for me.

I am writing this on Aurora's day. Would that nothing but a dawn parted us! Above all things, hold fast to this: *it must be if we will and act.* Do not mention this letter to anyone or everything may be ruined. And do not forget that "yes." I must have this assurance before I can think of anything further.

I mean all this as it stands, with my whole soul, and sign it with my name—Robert Schumann.

She looked for him when she came on stage an hour later, gazing for a moment with glistening eyes out over the audience. Then, as she had done one memorable time before, she quietly took her place at the piano, and with full heart, declared herself in the most ecstatic terms to her beloved "secret listener." All those who knew of the affair were as aware as Schumann of what was being poured into his *Symphonic Études* that August morning. The music was his, the interpretation hers, thus uniting them in this one way which her father could never prevent.

Not until the following day did Becker return to Schumann with a more formal reply:

You ask only for a simple "yes"? Such a little word—such an important one. Yet should not a heart so full of inexpressible love as mine be able to utter this little word with the whole soul? I do so, and my inmost being ever whispers it to you.

Could I describe the agonies of my heart, my many tears— oh, no! Perhaps fate decrees that we are soon to speak together, and then— And so once more I say to you, "yes!" Will God make my eighteenth birthday a day of sorrow? No, that would be too terrible. I, too, have long felt "it must be." Nothing in the world shall make me hesitate. I will show my father that a youthful heart can also be firm.

In great haste,

                                               Your Clara.

These words made Schumann almost wild with joy. But for him there remained one final test of her readiness. "I must have Clara's ring and she mine," he said to Becker, as he pulled his band from his finger. "Is it too much to ask, dear friend, that you act for us once again?"

"Are you betrothed?" Becker asked, smiling.

"If you come back to me with Clara's ring—yes! Hurry, Becker. You will be bringing me life itself!"

It was in this way that the secret engagement was carried out. And Becker's prize for having successfully conducted his romantic mission was a copy of Schumann's *Phantasiestuck des Abends* with the following inscription penned on the cover:

> To his dear Becker
>   Robert Schumann
> Shyly, but with affection, there signs herself
>   Clara Wieck.

Having exchanged rings, Schumann and Clara now awaited with the greatest impatience the fateful September thirteenth. They trembled to think that it could either bring to them the ultimate in joy, or a new time of trial and grief.

TWENTY-SEVEN

CLARA's first thought when she awoke the morning of her
birthday was of Robert. "Father will make him happy today," she said, smiling to herself. She dressed quickly with
as much care as if it were her wedding day, and went down,
in a joyous mood, to join her parents at breakfast. But inner
excitement, which she could barely suppress, did away with
her appetite. Nor had she the slightest patience for the usual
morning chatter at the table. Little tremors of happiness
mingled with apprehension made her afraid of giving herself
away. She soon excused herself and went into the parlor,
where for lack of anything else to do while she waited, she
picked up a book.

But reading too was impossible. All her faculties were concentrated elsewhere. She was listening for the sound of the
doorbell. Before Becker's departure, it had been agreed that
it was unwise for her to hand Robert's letter to her father
personally, as this might compromise her. The plan now was
for a messenger to deliver the letter some time before noon.
If her father, after reading its contents, were to show it to
her, she was to behave as if it came as a complete surprise,
but oh what a joyful one!

At last, at ten-thirty, the bell sounded. Nanny, who was in
Clara's confidence, ran down the stairs to open the door. But
to their disappointment, it was Frau Stegmayer, Clementine's
best friend. She bustled in, gave Clara a birthday kiss, and

settled herself down to spend the day. Before long, the two older women were exchanging trivialities in the room, while Clara, secretly annoyed by Frau Stegmayer's intrusion, resumed her "reading." Again not a single word was comprehensible.

What will Robert say in his letter? Will Father be angry? Dear heaven! It's so late— What if the messenger doesn't come at all? These were the only thoughts running through her mind. The suspense was agonizing.

The clock struck eleven. Her father, who was taking the day off, came out of his study with a newspaper in his hand. He told Frau Stegmayer that he had been busy going over the itinerary for Clara's winter tour, which was only a few weeks away.

"This time he's taking Clara to Vienna," Clementine said, smiling ruefully at her friend. "And she's going to play before the empress. Oh, how I'd love to be there—" She sighed with unmistakable envy. "But, as usual, Friedrich says it's out of the question."

"It is a pity always to be left behind," Frau Stegmayer said appealing to Wieck. "Why can't Nanny stay here to oversee the house and the children?"

"Clara wants Nanny with her," Wieck said. His tone brooked no argument. The two women meekly dropped the subject.

But he was in a good humor. He flourished his newspaper. "Those Viennese cannibals are already out to devour Clara," he said with a smirk. "Listen to what Bauerlie has to say in the *Theatrezeitung*: 'Vienna is soon to decide whether this modest young artist who in Germany ranks beside Liszt and Chopin, can be mentioned in the same breath with Thalberg.' Ha! What do you say to that, Clara?"

"I'm sorry. I didn't hear a word you said, Father."

"Well, put away your book, and read this instead," he said, handing her the paper. "You have to keep up with everything they say about you in this business. It's not vanity, it's *necessity*."

While she was reading, he lit a cigar. "Thalberg!" he said between puffs. "Why Clara is Thalberg and Henselt in one!"

It was at this moment that the bell sounded for a second time. In his jovial mood Wieck went to answer it himself. Clara froze in her chair. She imagined that Clementine and Frau Stegmayer could surely hear the wild beating of her heart. A moment later her father returned, holding a thick envelope between his fingers.

"Well! Schumann must think it's *my* birthday," he said, winking in Clara's direction. "He's written me a letter."

"Schumann?" Clementine wrinkled her brow. The name always gave a twinge to her conscience. "What can he want? Didn't he already thank you for presenting his *Études*?"

"Let him thank me again," Wieck said expansively. "I don't mind, as long as—" He didn't finish the sentence, but began to open the envelope.

Clara was far too nervous to say anything. She was conscious of Clementine's gaze toward her burning cheeks. She kept her eyes fixed on her father as he unfolded his letter. Another, smaller piece of paper, which had been enclosed, fell to the floor. Clementine quickly retrieved it.

"Why, it's for me," she said. "But what does it mean?" Slowly she read the note aloud:

"I commend our happiness, kind lady, to your heart—no stepmotherly heart, I think. Your clear sight, your good wishes, your great respect and love for Clara—"

Here Clementine paused, looked up for a moment to meet Clara's eyes, then resumed in a lower, less steady voice:

"—will make you find out the best way. Shall the birthday of a being who has already given happiness to such countless numbers be a day of sorrow? Ward off this great misfortune which threatens us all! Your most devoted,

Robert Schumann."

"What does it mean?" she repeated to Clara.

"Never mind! Clara knows nothing about it," Wieck answered quickly. Casually he put his own letter inside his pocket. "This is not her doing. But excuse us, *Liebchen*," he said, turning to Clara. He motioned Clementine and Frau Stegmayer to come with him. "We'll only be gone a few minutes."

The three disappeared into her father's study. The door was shut, and she was left sitting alone. The entire scene had infuriated her. It was an ominous beginning. Why should he invite that busybody, Frau Stegmayer, to partake of a private family matter, while *she*, who was most vitally concerned with the letter, was left to wait on the outside.

She paced the floor, glancing up now and then toward the room where her parents had locked themselves away. What were they talking about? Did they realize their decision was almost a matter of life and death for two people? What took them so long? "Patience!" she told herself. That had been Becker's last warning to her. And he was right. If she held her tongue, it was just barely possible that everything might turn out better than she thought. Any moment her father might come out smiling, and give her his blessing—

Suddenly there was a burst of laughter from inside the study. Instantly her cheeks flamed with indignation. Her father, whose voice now boomed out just loud enough to be heard, was making a mockery of Robert's letter:

"—I confess that I have never thought so calmly of my future as I do today. Secured against want, with fine plans in my head, a youthful heart inspired by all things noble, hands to work, a magnificent sphere of activity, and still in hopes of accomplishing everything that can be expected of my powers; honored and loved by many—is not all this enough? Ah, how painful an answer I must give to that! For what is it all compared to the pain of being parted from the very being for whom I strive, and who loves me in return, truly and from her heart! Ask her eyes if I do not speak the truth—"

"Is it a proposal?" Clara heard Frau Stegmayer ask. "I've never heard such language."

"Well, at least he's done it the proper way this time," Clementine said. "It's what he should have done in the first place. A lot of trouble could have been avoided."

"I haven't finished yet," said Wieck.

Clara stood as if paralyzed as he went on reading:

"For eighteen long months you have put me to the proof, as bitterly as fate could have done. Should I be angry with you? I had wounded you deeply. . . . But you have made me do penance. Try me now again. Perhaps I shall win back your confidence. You know that I persevere in high matters. If you find that I have been proved to be true and manly, bless this union of ours; for nothing but a parent's sanction is wanting to our happiness. It is no momentary excitement, nor blind passion. It is nothing merely external that binds me to Clara. It is the deep conviction that rarely has there been a union in which all the conditions of life are so favorable. . . ."

Here the voice broke off. There was a silence within, and then what seemed to be a conference in whispers. Clara realized now that her father had been deliberately reading loud enough for her to hear.

"Whatever you do, be composed!" she told herself sternly. "Don't let them see you cry. But if they can desecrate this moment, knowing how sacred it is to you, then do what *must* be done. Go to Robert in secret, write to him when and as you please! Defy them!" She choked back her tears of rage.

Vienna! If only it weren't so close at hand. But there was no way of avoiding it. Once again it meant a long, heartbreaking separation. But at least there was an understanding between Robert and herself. Their secret betrothal could sustain them. Afterward—

Wieck came out of the study, interrupting her thought. He had his hat and coat on. He nodded to her and then went on his way out of the house.

"Where is Father going?" she asked Clementine, trying to control her fury.

"To settle a piece of business," Clementine replied, not looking at her.

"If I'm not mistaken, that 'business' is also mine," Clara said imperiously. "I deserve some explanation—"

"Your father will settle it quite peacefully, Clara. I think it's a shame for Schumann to bother you just now when there's Vienna to consider—"

"And after Vienna, Paris!" Clara interrupted her angrily.

"But you yourself promised your father to devote a few more years to your art—"

"All we ask of Father is that he consent to our engagement. Robert and I know how to be reasonable."

Frau Stegmayer was embarrassed at being in the center of this exchange. She tried to think of something to say which would smooth things over. "It was a very romantic proposal," she said to Clara, smiling fatuously. "It's really too bad a man like that doesn't amount to more than he does. He *expresses* himself so well."

Clara was speechless with rage. She fled from the room. What was the use of talking in front of a woman who measured everything in terms of money?

In her own room, she sank down on her bed. Nanny murmured words of comfort, and brought wet towels to put on her head. "Oh, Nanny," she said despairingly, "if only my mother were here! Everything would be so much better." She tried to imagine what was going on now in Robert's room. It was the first time that he and her father had talked together since that long-ago Christmas Day. Her restlessness and anxiety increased with every passing moment. Remembering how savage her father's temper could be, she thought of putting on her cape and going after him. But what if, by some miracle, the talk was not going too badly? Robert, with his sweetness, had a persuasive way. Then she would have spoiled everything. Almost childishly she clung to the belief that, because it was her birthday, her father would not want to disappoint her. He would surprise everyone! He would come home and give his blessing as a gift—

An hour later he returned. As he did not come up to her, she immediately went downstairs, fully expecting him to invite her to have a talk with him. But he kept silent, acting as though his visit with Schumann was strictly his own business and none of her affair. Curiously, though, he was still in a good humor. There was nothing faintly resembling his previous wild behavior whenever Schumann, unwanted, intervened in his life. Seeing that she was miserably unhappy, he became solicitously tender but, at the same time, carefully avoided any mention of the *cause* of her unhappiness. At dinner, her official birthday celebration, he did his best to make her smile by telling odd little jokes. This, to Clara, was the greatest insult of all. Tears flooded her eyes at every word. She thought him cruel and boorish.

"Father," she said in a low voice, as the wine was being served, "won't you please tell me what happened when you saw Robert this afternoon? I have a right to know. . . ."

"Dry your tears," he whispered back sternly. "I won't have any more foolishness. It's ridiculous to spoil your birthday over nothing."

"Nothing! Oh, Father! If my birthday has been spoiled, it was *you* who did it!"

There was only one way now to find out the truth. Clara determined that at the first possible opportunity she would send Nanny to Schumann with a message. Later that night, she wrote a note to him, which Nanny carefully hid away inside her bonnet. It read: "If you have anything to say to me, tell it to my Nanny. As truly as I love you, so truly is she discreet."

The reply, which was smuggled back a few days later, almost broke her heart. It was blurred with tears, wildly incoherent in places, the handwriting alone indicating what torment and anger still raged in Robert's heart:

The interview with your father was terrible. Such coldness, such ill will, such confusion and contradictions! He knows how to annihilate me. He buries the knife in my heart up to the hilt!

Be forearmed, and do not let yourself be sold one day. I trust you, and that sustains me, but you will have to be strong, stronger than you have any idea. Your father himself said the terrible words that *nothing would move him!*

You have everything to fear from him, Clara. He will compel you by force if he does not succeed by craft. I am not so faint-hearted as to give you up, but I admit that I am so embittered, feel so *degraded*, so outraged in my most sacred feelings—that even your image has fled from me today—I can hardly picture your eyes. He treats me like dirt under his feet. . . .

He would concede nothing except that we might meet sometimes in public, not in your house ever, or mine; but in the presence of everybody to be stared at. We might also write to each other when you are traveling. How chilling it is! How it rankles!

In vain do I seek excuses for him. In vain look for nobler, deeper reasons for his refusal, such as that he fears that you would suffer as an artist because of an early engagement, or that you are altogether too young, and other such reasons. There is nothing to all this, believe me. *He would throw you to the first comer with enough money and rank.* Beyond this he has no higher idea than concert-giving and traveling. For this he saps your life, and shatters my strength in the midst of my endeavors to do something beautiful in the world. . . . May the good God comfort me, so that I may not be lost in despair. The roots of my life are withered. . . .

But his postscript, for which Clara was grateful, was calmer:

It is important that we advance quietly and carefully. I can see that. Eventually he must resign himself to the idea of losing you. His obstinacy will shatter itself against our love. When I asked him if he did not think we should be the happiest two people in the world, he conceded that, yet we got nowhere. He said that we should need far more money than we imagined, and named an enormous sum! Yet, believe me, Clara, together we have as much as a hundred of the most respected families here. Do not let him convince you otherwise. He also insisted that you would often shed tears in secret if we did not give large parties, etc. Clara, is that true? Is it not laughable? He could not, and cannot bring forward anything which has a real foundation. Right and reason are on our side. If he drives us to extremes, if, in another year and a half or two years, he still refuses to recognize us, we must seek our right. The authorities will marry us. But heaven forbid that it ever come to that!

Before I take leave of you today, my beloved, swear to me once more, by your salvation, that you have courage bravely to withstand the trials that are laid upon us, as I do, at this moment, lifting up the two fingers of my right hand in token that I take the oath. I will never forsake you! Rely on me. And so, may God help us both—

I remain forever

Your Robert.

TWENTY-EIGHT

Now BEGAN a time when correspondence became their only link, and even this had to be arranged in secret so that Wieck, whom Clara no longer trusted, could not intercept their letters. For the better part of six months, a lonely winter turning into a still more lonely spring, messages of love, despair and hope went back and forth across the border.

It was a time, under the safety of distance, for the most microscopic probing of their individual emotions. The strain of separation brought into the open old doubts and hesitations Clara thought she had long since resolved. She tormented herself, and Schumann still more, with repetition of her father's arguments, which she was again forced to listen to daily during the long Vienna tour. Her letters, testing these arguments, sometimes only in order to hear Schumann's reassuring reply, were filled with contradictions and vacillation. It was such a time as could have separated them forever.

Nov. 3, 1837: Clara to Robert

. . . We left Dresden last Sunday. The morning was so beautiful, the Elbe so clear with the sky reflected in it, and the sun looked at me in a friendly way as if it would say, "Give me your greeting, I will take it to him faithfully." I could picture to myself so vividly how shyly it would glide through the park to your window. . . .

I am very distressed to see how unhappy Father is when he thinks of losing me. I am conscious of my duty to him, and yet I love you without measure! He thinks I should forget you. Forget! The word makes me shudder. He does not know the strength of a loving heart . . . my spirit is always with you, the knot is made fast. I will never undo it. . . .

Nov. 12, 1837: *Clara to Robert*

. . . Why do you write to me that your hopes are "sinking"? Is that the meaning you draw from my letters? Ah, Robert, that hurts. Let this go no further! Let us suppose for a moment that a diamond appeared which so blinded me that I could no longer see Eusebius, Florestan and the rest, and you were one day to read in the paper: "Engagement of Fräulein Clara Weick to Herr von Rope-of-Pearls, or Diamond Tiara." . . .

But seriously, Robert, am I a little child who will suffer herself to be led to the altar as if to school? No! When you call me a child, that sounds so dear; but when you *think* me a child, then I stand up and say: *You are mistaken!*

You want to know something of my life. Listen, then. Today I gave a concert in the Conservatoire and I was recalled thirteen times. Great heavens! I never saw such enthusiasm before. You can imagine that I did not know what to do. Again and again I had to come out of my hiding place, and there were all the curtsies, which you know I do so abominably!

Nov. 17, 1837: *Clara to Robert*

At last, after nearly a week, I manage to write a few words to you again. Do not think that is easy, for I have to write to you with my door unlocked as Father is very angry if he finds the room locked. And how suspicious he is now! Think! He told Nanny: "I know the dodge, and how to find out if Clara has written to Schumann—it will not remain concealed from me long."

It will be best if you address your next letter to a gentleman, "Herr Julius Kraus, *Poste Restante*," at Vienna, of course. But let the address always be written by Dr. Reuter. . . .

Yesterday my second concert took place before an audience of nearly 600 in spite of the fact that the whole aristocracy is not here yet, and there was another storm of applause. . . .

What makes you think that I cannot bear your *Davidsbundler Dances?* So far I have not been able to get two hours' peace to myself to dedicate to them and they need that. None but I could decipher such writing!

Now, good night. The tea is ice-cold, the room grows colder and colder, but I grow warmer and warmer. . . .

Nov. 24, evening: Clara to Robert

Tomorrow we set out for Vienna by the flying coach. You will get this letter on Monday, which gives you a week in which you can write much and *clearly!*

I have been thinking a great deal about my circumstances during these days, and I must call your attention to something.

You rely on the ring! Good heavens, that is but an external bond. Had not Ernestine too a ring from you and, what is of more importance, your promise? And yet you tore that bond asunder. The ring is of no consequence.

One thing I must say to you. I cannot be yours until circumstances have entirely altered. I do not want horses or diamonds— I am happy in possessing you. But I wish to lead a life free from care, and I see that I shall be unhappy if I cannot always work at my art. And that I cannot do if we have to worry over our daily bread. I require much, and I realize that much is needed for a comfortable life.

Therefore, Robert, ask yourself if you are in a condition to offer me a life free from care. Think, that, simply as I have been brought up, I have yet never had a care, and am I to bury my art now?

Ah, God! I feel as if my heart would burst. You are not angry

with me, are you? I do not know what I want. . . . I feel as if
I had done something to you. . . .

Nov. 28, 1837: Robert to Clara

*You can never be mine unless circumstances have completely
altered!* Clara, your father's spirit stood behind you and dictated
that! But you have written it, and you are right to think of your
external happiness. We must be quite clear about this.

The only thing that troubles me is that you make the objection
now, for the first time, which you should have made to me when
I first frankly explained my circumstances to you. It would
certainly never have entered my head to write to your father if
I thought that you still had so many scruples—

No, my wealth is not overpowering, but such that many a girl,
even many a pretty and good one, might give me her hand on it
and say, "it will be hard to make both ends meet, but you shall
find me a good housekeeper," etc., etc. At one time you thought
so too. Perhaps now you think differently. My mind reels.

To business: unless a gift falls from heaven, I do not see how
I can increase my income in a short time, as much as, on your
account, I wish I could. You know the kind of work I do. You
know that it is purely intellectual, that it cannot be carried on
any moment like manual labor. I have shown that I can persevere. Mention any young fellow of my age who has made for
himself so wide a sphere of activity in so short a time. It goes
without saying that I should like to extend it, to earn more, and
in this I shall not fail. But I do not believe that this will achieve
as much as you wish, or as you perhaps have now.

On the other hand, I can, with a clear conscience, rely upon
being able to support one wife, or even two wives, in about two
years' time without any great anxiety, though certainly not without
continuing to work. As I said, your father held the pen—the
coldness of the lines has something killing in it. Now, too, that
you think so little of my ring, since yesterday I have cared no more
for yours and no longer wear it.

I dreamed that I was walking by a deep pool—an impulse seized me, and I threw the ring into it. I will write more to-morrow. My head is on fire and my eyes are heavy with grief over you. Farewell, however. . . .

Nov. 29th: Robert to Clara

To think it is possible to torment oneself so over a few hundred pieces of silver a year which are still lacking to us! You know what I have. I need only half for myself. If the other half is not enough for you, you will easily earn something yourself. It all depends on how we contrive.

Here is what I plan. I should prefer to keep my present inde-pendent position for a time, have a nice house not far from the town, you with me, work and live happily and quietly with you. You would, of course, practice your great art, as ever, but less for the sake of anybody and everybody and on account of the money than for the sake of a few elect, and on account of our happiness. A life such as this requires no great expenditure. If you would be happy in it, neither you nor I can know. People alter; chance and fate often spoil a good game.

It will be another thing if you want to live for the great world. I would agree to that too. In that case we would let our house stand empty for three months (I could be away as long as that every year, provided I can go on editing the newspaper) and travel, now to Paris, now to London. You have a reputation everywhere and I have friends and numerous connections. In short, honor and profit could not be wanting, and we should come back to our house (which, alas, is still nonexistent) richly laden with treasure. . . .

Oh, beautiful pictures! May no one shatter you to pieces! If only I, for once, lay happy on your loving heart. All these nights of anguish, sleepless with the thought of you—a merciful God must repay them some day.

You say rather harshly that I tore asunder the bond with Ernestine. That is not true. It was unloosed in due form with the consent of both of us. But with respect to this dark page in my life, I will some day lay bare to you a deep secret, a severe mental suffering which befell me. It occupied a long time and includes the years from the summer of 1833 onwards. You shall know all about it some day—

I have still much to say to you: First, what would you do if your father discovered our correspondence? Give me a decided answer to this. Do not be frightened if he talks about disinheriting and such things. He cannot deprive you of your heart. Then, too, you have a mother. If ever he tries to force you, there is your natural refuge. If he finds us out, will you still go on writing to me? *If you allowed yourself to be frightened, as you did in Dresden, if you gave me no sign . . . Clara, I would not seek for you a second time, never again. . . .*

Chopin is seriously ill. Mendelssohn told me so yesterday. We were at the Voigts'.

Dec. 6, 1837: *Clara to Robert*

. . . Could you so wound me, draw from me such bitter tears? Is it Robert who so misunderstood me, who read so ugly a meaning into my words? Have I deserved this?

Yes, I know that many beautiful and perhaps as good girls as I are at your disposal, and better housewives than any artist is supposed to be. Yes, I know it, but it is not well that you should mention such a thought to me. . . .

You think I harbor unattainable wishes. I want but two things, your heart and your happiness. How could I be calm if you were burdened with cares on my account? My imagination can picture no fairer happiness than to continue living for art, but quietly, so that we may both owe many a pleasant hour to it.

So we agree in all things, and I fall upon your heart and say, "Yes, Robert, let us live like this." . . .

Dec. 12, 1837: *Clara to Robert*

. . . At last I have an evening at home again, and can chat with you. With rather a beating heart I am looking forward to my first concert here. Vienna is quite different from what people say abroad. There are distinguished connoisseurs here and innumerable amateurs with a real taste for art. They know everything of Chopin's and understand him—but very little of Henselt, though they are getting to know him through me, and are amazed to hear that he lived here for three years. Mendelssohn is almost wholly unknown; his *Lieder ohne Worte* lie untouched in the music shops. They do not sing here! His *Midsummer Night's Dream Overture* was not at all liked. I wanted to play something of his at my first concert, but I dare not.

Your works find a great upholder in Professor Fischof, especially since he heard me play some of them. He is your only friend, otherwise they are all your enemies. I cannot get a copy of your paper to read. . . . The most terrible of all questions is always: "Who is this Schumann? Where does he live? Does he play the piano? What are his compositions like?" Then I want to say, like you, "He is a person with whom you have nothing at all to do, who stands so far above you that you are incapable of understanding him." . . .

Ah, Robert, believe me, I have many sorrowful hours. No pleasure is complete to me when you are not there! How many polite things I have to say to people, and all the while I am conscious of nothing but the thought of you.

Dec. 15, 1837: *Clara to Robert*

. . . Do not judge Father harshly because of what I write about him. He does not now try to persuade me to give you up, because he knows that it hurts my feelings, depresses and disheartens me, and makes it difficult for me to give concerts and to practice. . . .

It hurts me when you wish to cast a stone at Father because he wishes for some small recompense for all the hours which he has devoted to me. He wishes me to be happy, and thinks that is to be obtained by riches. Can you be angry with him for it? He loves me above all things, and would not thrust me, his child, away from him if he saw that my happiness could be founded on you alone. So, for love of me, forgive him his natural vanity. Consider he has treated you like this only for love of me. You, too, love me, and you make me happy when you forgive him. I would not have him misunderstood by you. Every man has his faults; I have and so have you—you will allow me to say so!

Now, for another question—why do you avoid every opportunity of mentioning me in your paper? Father is now very unhappy to think that I love you. He is never really tender, he quickly becomes cold at the thought that my heart beats for another; he cannot imagine that I can be happy with you, for he says, "If Schumann does nothing for Clara under these present circumstances, will he do anything when he is married?"

Your secret makes me very anxious about you, Robert, what am I to understand by this?

December 21, 1837: Clara to Robert

. . . My second concert took place today and was certainly another triumph. When one has been here, one never wants to go North again, where men have hearts of stone (you are, of course, excepted). You ought to listen to a storm of applause here. I had to repeat the Bach *Fugue* and the Henselt *Variations*. No pleasanter feeling than that of having satisfied a whole audience.

So much for me. Now for you. I had to laugh at the place in your letter where you write, "And so we will come back to our house laden with treasures." Good heavens! What are you thinking of? Treasures are no longer to be got by instrumental art. How much one has to do in order to bring away a few *Thaler* from a town. When you are sitting with Poppe at 10 o'clock in the evening, or are going home, I, poor thing, am arriving at a party where I have to play to people for a few pretty words and a cup of warm water and get home, dead tired, at 11 or 12 o'clock, drink a draught of water, lie down, and think, "Is an artist much more than a beggar?"

And yet art is a fine gift! What, indeed, is finer than to clothe one's feelings in music, what a comfort in time of trouble, what a pleasure, what an exquisite feeling to give happy hours to so many people by its means! And what an exalted feeling so to follow art that one gives one's life to it!

Yes, I am happy, but shall be perfectly so only when I can fling myself on your heart and say, "Now I am yours forever— I and my art."

Christmas Eve, 1837: Clara to Robert

. . . How can I better celebrate Christmas Eve than by talking to you? I was very sad today, because my eye fell on no Christmas tree. Where may you be now? Are you very happy? But yes—for the tree of love flames for you! One thought has occupied me today: how will things be with us in three years' time? Perhaps you too have been thinking the same. . . .

On Tuesday (the day after tomorrow) I am to play to the Empress. I have had a reception here which has made up for the mortifications which I received in the North. You may already have heard of one delicate attention towards me. Schubert left behind, among other things, a *Duo* for four hands which has just been printed by Diabelli, and dedicated to me. This has affected me very much, I can hardly say why, myself. . . .

Liszt is not yet here, but is daily expected . . . At my next concert I am going to play Beethoven's *F minor sonata* and afterwards, privately, your *Carnaval*. Are not the *Phantasiestücke* nearly ready? I should have liked, dear Robert, to have worked you a little remembrance for Christmas, but do I not employ my time better when I write to you?

December 26, 11 o'clock: Clara to Robert

. . . It is late, but I must send a few words. I have just come from the Empress, I am eating a plate of soup, and will finish my letter. Although the Emperor, the Empress, and the rest have been talking to me, do you not think that I would rather talk to you?

Yesterday Father again said to Nanny, "If Clara marries Schumann, I would say upon my death-bed that she is not worthy to be my daughter." . . . Robert, does not that hurt? My feelings cannot be described. . . . I tell you this only because it moves my heart too deeply for me to keep silent about it to you.

I am quite beside myself when I hear Father raging in the evening . . . when his curses rouse me from sleep, and I hear them aimed at my dearest. *I am no longer so fond of my father.* Ah, God! I can no longer be so whole-heartedly affectionate, and yet I should so like to be. It is Father whom I have to thank for everything. . . . To your question whether I will allow myself to be frightened again by him, the answer is: No, never again!

January 2, 1838: Robert to Clara

How happy you have made me by your last letters, and in the first place by the one on Christmas Eve. I could call you by every possible term of endearment, but I know no better word than the little German "dear." . . . If only, my Clara, I could do something for love of you. The old knights were better off. They could pass through the fire for their beloved or slay dragons, but we of the present day must try to serve our ladies by scraping farthings together and smoking fewer cigars, and such things.

But truly, the knights notwithstanding, we know how to love, and in this, as in all things, the times alone have changed and hearts remain the same.

I have my terrible hours too, when even your image forsakes me, when I ask myself, with reproaches, if I have guided my life as wisely as I might have done, if I did right in chaining you, angel that you are, to me; if I can make you as happy as I should. Your father's treatment of me is the cause of all these questions and doubts. A man easily thinks himself what others think him to be. After the way your father has treated me, I am forced to ask myself, "Are you so bad then? Are you so base that a man can treat you like this?" If I am repulsed, insulted, slandered— I used to read of such things in novels, but I thought myself too good ever to become the hero of such a family drama. If I had ever injured your father, well then, he might hate me; but that he should abuse me for absolutely no reason, and, as you yourself say, hate me, that I cannot understand. But my turn will come some day—and then he shall see how I love him and you. For, let me whisper it in your ear, I love and honor your father for his many great and noble qualities—it is a peculiar, innate attachment on my part, a submission which I feel toward him, as I do toward all energetic natures. This doubles my pain, now that he will have no more to do with me.

Well, perhaps peace will come now, and he will say to us, "Well, take each other."

March 3, 1838: Clara to Robert

. . . I talked to Father a great deal about you today, and he told me that he was quite inclined to be friendly to you when we came back. You are to be the friend of the house again, and he told me that he had written to you privately from Dresden to say that he would never give his consent if we remain in Leipzig, but that he certainly would if we moved into any other large city. I have promised him that I would never remain in Leipzig, but that I could never love anyone but you. He gave me his consent and wrote it in my diary: *March 3rd, early conversation with Clara about Schumann, that I will never give my consent to Leipzig, and Clara quite agrees with me, and her view will never alter. Schu. can opera-tize philosophize, be as enthusiastic, idealize as much as he likes. It remains settled that Clara can never live in poverty and obscurity, but must have over 2000 Thaler a year to spend.*

Consider, dear Robert, I cannot earn three *Pfennig* by my art in Leipzig, and you too would have to work yourself to death in order to earn what we need. . . . Let us do as Father suggests. We will come here, or you can come first, give your paper to Diabelli, Haslinger (a very respectable firm) or Mechetti (a vigorous and enterprising young man). In the first place, your work will be paid as well; in the second, you are certainly far more recognized and respected here than in Leipzig; and in the third, it is such a pleasant, cheap life here, that is, of course, considering the size of the town. What beautiful surroundings! And then, I too am thought far more of here than in Leipzig. I am received by the highest aristocracy, loved at court and by the public. I can give a concert every winter which will bring me 1000 *Thaler* (easily) with the high prices of admission which they have here. Then I can, and will, give a lesson every day that will bring in another 1000 *Thaler* during the year, and you have 1000, what more do we want?

In a word, we can lead the happiest life here. . . . Father spent an hour today in placing before me everything that I have written to you. He even said, "If Schumann does not like to be a long time in Vienna without you, I will do this for him, I will go with you to Vienna."

You see from this that Father is quite kind. So do not be cold toward him. He wishes us well. He quite realizes that I will never give my heart to another, and to give my hand without my heart—a father like mine does not do such things.

Leipzig, March 17, 1838: Robert to Clara

Your letter raised me from one joy to another. What a life you open before me, what prospects! As I read your letter again and again, I feel as the first man may well have felt when his angel led him through the new, young creation from height to height, and at last said to him: "All this is yours."

Shall all this be mine? Do you not know that it is one of my oldest and most cherished wishes that it should some day be possible to live for a number of years in the city in which the noblest in art was called forth, the city in which Beethoven and Schubert lived?

Shake hands then—our minds are made up. . . . When we go away together it will be as if morning and evening bells sounded at once, but the morning bells are prettier. And then you will rest on my heart, the happiest heart! *It is decided—we go!*

Oh, Clara, there is so much music in me now, and such beautiful melodies always. Just think, I have finished another whole volume of new things. *Kreisleriana* I shall call it; you and the thought of you play the chief part, and I will dedicate it to you. . . . And I must not forget to mention another thing. . . . Was it an echo of what you once said when you wrote that I often seemed like a child to you?—in short, I felt as if I were in pinafores again and then I wrote 30 quaint little things, about twelve of which I have selected and called *Kinderscenen* [Scenes from Childhood]. You will enjoy them, but you will have to forget that you are a virtuoso—

Now, if only it were possible to win the love and confidence of your father, whom I would so gladly call Father, whom I have to thank for so much of the joy of my life, for advice and also for sorrow. Well, the pain is over. It is forgiven. He is your father, he has brought you up in the noblest way. He would like to weigh out the happiness of your future in a balance to know that you were quite happy and safe, as you always have been under his protection. I cannot blame him. In truth he wants you to have the best there is on earth.

What you write to me of him, that he talked to you quietly in our favor has surprised and delighted my heart. But forgive my suspicion: Is it possible that he only wants to get me out of Leipzig? I should not like to give up my life in Leipzig until a word from him has made me certain of you. But, nevertheless, Vienna remains my goal. . . .

TWENTY-NINE

ONE YEAR LATER, sitting in a coach which was about to take off for Nuremberg, Clara had cause to remember Schumann's words, "the pain is over." All around her were strangers settling down for an uncomfortable winter journey. Outside, great pearls of snow, blown about by a gusty wind, were caught in the shining haze of street lamps. Soon Leipzig would be left behind. Soon, in the thickening dusk, the postilion's horn would sound its last farewell.

"And I," Clara whispered inwardly, "will be sounding mine."

Much had happened since the glorious days in Vienna, much that was causing her to ask: *but is pain ever over, or does it just begin when the tide carries you out into the center of life, into the lights of the world?*

The Austrians had heaped upon her more riches than she had ever dreamed. The gates of the Imperial Palace swung open and she was declared *Pianiste Extraordinaire* to the Emperor, an unprecedented honor for a girl and a Protestant. Franz Liszt, whose creative fingers aroused fire and thunder from the keys, bowed before her power and could not restrain wild applause when he heard her. Even the Viennese poets publicly sang her praise.

Yet all these honors, the acclaim and adulation, had become meaningless the moment she discovered the falseness of her father's promise in regard to Robert. He had made it,

as soon became obvious, merely to keep her content while
performing, or, as Schumann put it, "to give her a pleasant
hour in Vienna."

In May, when they returned to Leipzig, he was back to his
old stubborn story, refusing to welcome Schumann as a "friend
of the house" or anything else. And this time she did not
blame Robert for condemning him in the strongest possible
words:

I think he is a Philistine, wholly encrusted by material thoughts
and interests, who has become entirely devoid of human feeling.
Hatred toward him often rises in me again, so deep a hatred, it
does indeed look strange beside my love for his daughter.

That summer, though there was no border separating them,
they were again forced to resort to smuggled letters and
clandestine meetings, Nanny and Alwin acting as couriers.
But Robert despised having to see her in dark corners as if
he were some kind of low criminal. It took all the joy out of
his love. He brooded and sulked, and often cried out that
he would rather not see her at all than constantly to debase
himself by deception. Their brief times together, rather than
happy, became bitter-sweet; the partings unbearable. Finally,
in desperation, they came to a decision. Since her father was
no longer to be trusted, they must act on their own, make
their own plans and abide by them. It was agreed between
them that Robert go to Vienna as originally planned, establish
himself there; then she, regardless of her father's consent,
would join him no later than Easter 1840. In October, not
without trepidation, Robert uprooted his life in Leipzig for
her sake.

Now, three months later, she too was seeing the last of
Leipzig. Her usual winter tour was about to begin, this time
with Paris as her destination. How eagerly she had looked

forward to it up until now. The thought of seeing Uncle
Eduard again delighted her. Also two good friends were there,
Emilie List who had gone with her family to live in France,
and Pauline Garcia, a charming young singer whom she had
met during the previous summer. The city of Paris was itself
an enticement! Yet, now, nervously turning her handbag in
her fingers, cold even in her warmest cloak, she sat dreading
the moment of departure. For when the wheels turned in
the new snow, when the horses started down the long, dark
highway, then, in that moment of motion, it would be too
late to turn back. For the first time she was going on tour
alone.

"Isn't that Clara Wieck?" she heard someone whisper behind her.

"Yes, but where is her father?" came the reply. "She never
goes anywhere without him."

And that, thought Clara, stiffening, is the story of my
life.

It was true that her father was not sitting beside her. In his
place sat the "horrid" Frenchwoman whom he had hired to
be her companion. But it was true, too, that her heart
hungered for him this moment in a way she had little suspected it might a week ago when, in anger, she had defiantly
accepted his challenge: "Either give up Schumann or go to
Paris without me!" As well as he knew that such a threat
was not likely to change her, she was convinced that he would
not really abandon her. Paris meant too much to him. Besides, he would not think of letting her make such a long,
dangerous journey alone.

But apparently she had been wrong. For any moment now
the coach would be starting, and he was nowhere to be seen.
Bravely as she had said good-by to him, tearlessly as she had

accepted his cold kiss on her cheek and heard his last words,
"Take care, Clara," never had she been more frightened in her
life than she was now. "He is only testing me," she had
thought, when she left him. "He'll be along soon." But now
she was desperate. And the pity of it was that, if he were
suddenly to appear on the scene and open his arms to her,
she would probably crawl into them like a child and cry as a
child cries when it has been lost for a long time and finally
found again.

Yet what had he not done to her! One blow had followed
after another. He had even dismissed her adored Nanny, ordering her out of the house, never to return again. And all because Nanny, out of loyalty and love, had carried a letter for
her to Schumann. Poor, faithful Nanny, whose life was her
"Clärchen," her *"Liebchen,"* her "little dear." The very
thought of her desolate, without a home, without a position,
tore Clara apart. Yet she was powerless, powerless to do anything except what she was doing now:

Leave them, [Schumann had urged her] I could not help smiling
a little as I read in your letter that they promised you that you
should lead the happiest life if you would give me up. They will
dress you in gay clothes, and take you about the town and give
you oranges to eat. That is what *they* mean by a happy life. I can
say nothing except leave them at once!

"Now it has come to that," Clara thought sadly. The last
passenger was seated. The postilion mounted to position, making ready to sound his horn. And at the same moment chimes
from St. Thomas' began their Vesper call. She searched des-
perately through the gathering darkness. *Come now, Father,
now before it is too late,* her heart called out, quickening with
hope and fear.

But the silent snow fell, and all sounds died away except the sudden forward motion of the wheels, and one final cry which she alone could hear: *Farewell—farewell.*

The Frenchwoman (Clara determined to think of her by no other name) proved valuable in one respect. Her constant attendance forced Clara to face up to all her troubles on the journey without openly displaying fear. For on no account would she have this "spy" of her father's write to him that "Clara quailed."

I shall not be a coward in her eyes, Clara swore to herself. As a result, many whom she met in towns along the way thought her bold, indeed far too bold for a young girl. She was conscious of critical eyes, and sometimes even heard the acid comments: "Look! She travels alone! So that's the kind of life these artist-women lead!"

Ah, if only they knew what trembling lay beneath her calm exterior. What she had to endure, and how she hated it. In the first place, the traveling was either far more hazardous this brutal winter than ever before, or else it was only that when her father was along, she had not taken notice of the dangers. On the road to Nuremberg the thick downfall of snow entirely obliterated the horizon. Worse, the road itself. The coach went helter-skelter across fields and ditches. "We were in danger of our lives ten times," she told Schumann afterward. "How often did I pray to God that He would let us get happily through it all just this once more. . . ."

Then, there was the superiority of the men she had to deal with, whose smiles only faintly covered their cynicism. A woman, so young, managing her own tour! What temerity! But as Clara knew that many of them were in direct contact with her father and were likely to report to him any signs of weakness or failure on her part in the handling of her affairs, she proudly ignored all offers of assistance and staunchly carried through by herself each detail concerning her concerts, arranging for the hall, distributing free tickets, finding responsible piano movers and tuners. In Nuremberg it all had to be done in one week, for her first concert was arranged for January fifteenth.

Would she ever forget that terrible day? After all the hard work, and planning, she awoke to discover herself helplessly marooned by a flood! There was no getting out of the house. She was forced to sit the whole day in her room, locked in with her hated companion. But she took solace in telling her troubles to the only person to whom she would dare admit discouragement or defeat.

Think, Robert! Not only have I nearly been snowed in, but we are right in the water and cannot get out. Indeed, the whole town is under water, for the river has overflowed, and is rising visibly. Many strangers have come here for my concert, but it is impossible now for it to take place. It must be put off. . . .

She could not help wondering as she wrote if her father, despite snow, flood, or whatever, would not have found a way to avoid "putting it off." Nature seldom daunted him. I can see him smiling to himself when he hears of it, she admitted to herself with some chagrin, and saying, "See! This is how Clara gets along without me."

In Stuttgart too, technical difficulties pursued her every step of the way. She failed altogether in her efforts to secure a theater and had to wait fifteen impatient days before learning that she might, at least, play at court. Her anguish was increased during this interval by the fact that since leaving Leipzig she had not had a single letter from home to sustain or encourage her. Robert's mail, as she understood, was being forwarded to a special box in Paris. But her father! Did he truly care so little as not to write at all?

Late at night, while the "Frenchwoman" lay calmly sleeping, Clara sat up confessing her loneliness and fright to Schumann.

. . . if he leaves me like this in a foreign land, without news, without everything, I do not know what I shall do. I do not even know whether I should go to Paris after all. My situation is really dreadful. I am supposed to arrive in Paris at the end of January. My God! What shall I do there alone?

But by morning her spirit revived. She awoke, facing with stern determination her tight-lipped companion who was resentful at being given only the most menial tasks to perform. Little wonder that the "horrid Frenchwoman" did not like Clara. They made most incompatible companions.

One day, from a bookseller in Hof, Clara accidentally learned a piece of news that filled her with joy.

"Ernestine is married!" she wrote to Schumann excitedly, "To a Count Zedwitz! I could not believe it. I wrote to her at once begging her to tell me all that has happened to her. Ah, my dear, if it be true, then we could enjoy our happiness as well again. . . ."

Not until she wrote those lines did she realize how heavy had been the guilt lying on her heart in respect to Ernestine. For now it was as though a tremendous burden was lifted, and she felt truly free to love and be loved by Robert.

This feeling brought about a change in her. It gave her the first sense of happiness she had had since leaving home. Suddenly she became quite genuinely cheerful. In her management of "Clara Wieck," to the relief of the local musicians, she carried on efficiently but with less rigidity and fear. She relaxed, and began to enjoy herself a little. There were many acquaintances of her father's in Stuttgart, some of whom had already sought her out, but toward whom she had behaved with aloofness and suspicion. Now she returned their calls more graciously, and visited others whom she had not yet seen. One, a well-known music teacher, Dr. Gustav Schilling, welcomed her so warmly that until the day she crossed the border into France, she found herself spending most of her free time in his home.

One afternoon he told her he would like her to stay long enough to listen to one of his pupils who was arriving in a few minutes.

"She is an able pianist," he said, "but comes from a poor family and has not had many opportunities. What a difference it would make to her if someone like you, Clara, were to take an interest in her."

The idea of appraising a pupil for her friend delighted Clara. Within a very few moments she was sitting in a comfortable wing chair in his studio, listening attentively to Schilling's young protégée. She liked what she heard, but even more what she saw. Henriette Reichmann, whose eyes were an odd mixture of yellow and green, whose light-colored hair, without a wave, was simply arranged in a bun at the nape of her neck, had a certain expression of sweetness about the mouth that reminded Clara of her mother. She also seemed to have a modesty so appealing that it was impossible not to take a sympathetic liking to her. She played one movement of a Mozart *Sonata*, and during the performance, which demonstrated a promising talent, an idea suddenly occurred to Clara. She could barely wait for Henriette to conclude in order to discuss it with Dr. Schilling.

"Well, what do you think of her?" he asked when Henriette had finished the piece. Henriette, too honest to do otherwise, kept her eyes fastened anxiously on Clara's face to learn from her expression rather than her words, her true opinion.

Clara met her gaze, and asked, "How old are you, Fräulein Reichmann?"

"Seventeen."

"Is it your ambition to continue your musical studies?"

"Oh, yes! Only I'm uncertain of my talent."

"Well, it's hard to tell at one hearing, but I don't think you need worry about that. You have a good, warm tone, and you caught the spirit of the music splendidly. What you need most of all is self-assurance."

"I know," Henriette agreed. "Dr. Schilling always tells me, 'have confidence,' but then I heard *you*, Fräulein Wieck, and I've been discouraged ever since. I'm sure such virtuosity will never be mine."

Clara laughed. "Let me tell you a secret. Last year when I was in Vienna I had the good fortune to hear both Liszt and Thalberg play and afterward, believe me, I, too, was ready to give up. I was so discouraged that I wrote to a friend, 'Since I have heard and seen Liszt's bravura, I feel like a schoolgirl!' So, you see, we musicians all have the same troubles. We never think we do well enough. But then, in the long run, that is what keeps us striving. Perhaps some day I shall play as well as Liszt and Thalberg, and you will play as well as I do."

Dr. Schilling rose to dismiss his pupil. "I would like to see you again," Clara told her, as they were saying good-by. "I have something in mind for you, but first I'd like to have Dr. Schilling's opinion. Can you come this same time tomorrow?"

Henriette turned eagerly to her teacher. "May I?"

"By all means," he said, smiling. "Do as Fräulein Wieck says. And don't let anything or anyone hold you up. I had a feeling that if I brought you two together something would come of it."

"I want to take that girl to Paris with me," Clara exclaimed excitedly as soon as Henriette had gone. "You can't imagine, Dr. Schilling, how much it would mean to me, how much I need such a companion. A girl my own age, who is sincere, capable and trustworthy— I could give her lessons and she could be of aid to me in dozens of ways."

Clara was visualizing the relief of an Henriette to offset the Frenchwoman. Financing another person was of course a problem, but she would think of some way to overcome that.

Dr. Schilling shook his head thoughtfully. "I don't know," he said, surprised at the extent of Clara's offer, "this is a girl who has never set foot outside of Stuttgart. She's a novice in the ways of the world; she's simple and inexperienced."

"All the better," Clara cried. "I don't think I should want a person who might dominate me. It will do me good to hold the reins for once, and yet have someone whom I like and trust. At first sight of Henriette, I said to myself, 'If I were to have a dear friend from whom I wouldn't like to part— this would be the one.' "

"Your judgment is sound," Dr. Schilling assured her. "But taking her away! Uprooting her altogether, and to Paris of all places! Her father, who fairly worships the girl, will most likely say no."

Clara was not to be put off. Wanting Henriette with her now more than ever, she pursued the point right to the father's doorstep. A few days later she was writing triumphantly to Vienna:

Tomorrow evening I'm off to Karlsruhe, and the day after I shall probably be playing to the Grand Duchess; then we go to Strassburg, stay there Sunday night, and next, Paris! You will receive this letter through Dr. Schilling. Answer him in a friendly manner as he means kindly. He is also the cause of my taking a young and talented girl with me to Paris. She is so fond of me that she left her parents no peace. Her father is poor but is ready to spend everything on her. It was touching when he came to me with tears in his eyes and said, "I am trusting to you the dearest thing that I possess." I could not help crying. The thought that I may perhaps bring happiness to Henriette makes me far happier than it can make her. I intend to give her as much attention as I can, for she has talent. I believe I have acted as you would wish, have I not, my dear, good Robert?

Clara was thinking of something he had once said to her: one ought not to be too absorbed in oneself and one's own interests, or one loses one's keenness of perception for the world around. He had been referring to his own introspection then, but she thought it applied to herself as well. She was so preoccupied with her personal ambition, and lately her own sorrows, particularly her heartache at the separation from her father, that she seldom gave thought to the rest of the world. Now, to train and look after Henriette would give her someone besides herself to think about.

On the eve of her departure for Paris, she was writing happily to Robert from Strassburg:

My heart is ever so much lighter now that I have a real friend with me, who understands me, to whom I have confided everything, and who is the best girl in all Stuttgart. She is very fond of me. She sends you word that she will not be happy until I am. I cannot be so bad when everybody is so fond of me. *I see now that I can stand alone in the world without my father,* and things will not remain as they are much longer. Soon, soon, I shall be with you, and then I shall know no sorrow, only what is yours shall be mine. Heaven wishes me well. Has it not just given me another dear friend? And some day it will give me the dearest friend of all.

A thousand kisses from your faithful bride.

Clara Schumann

"Oh! name of exquisite delights!"

But, as Paris was to prove to Clara, she had yet a little further to go before she could say these words, "I can stand alone in the world without my father," and really mean them. Schumann's long, lonely wait for her was not altogether Wieck's doing. Clara was like a girl clinging to the ribbons of a Maypole. As long as she held fast, she danced. What would happen to her once she released her fingers for good and all—of that she was still secretly terrified. It would have been a far more accurate reflection of her state of mind had she added a postscript: "But I still expect, and *hope* to find Father waiting for me in Paris. Oh, if so, what a relief, what a wonderful surprise!"

THIRTY

EDUARD FECHNER, with his yellow scarf pulled well around his throat, and the collar of his topcoat dusted with snow, turned in on the rue Michadière and stood for a moment looking uneasily at No. 7, the Hôtel where his niece had taken private rooms. He had not yet quite made up his mind how to tackle a wild-hearted, stubborn girl who went running off from home to do and live exactly as she pleased. The letter from her father which was stuffed in his pocket described Clara as "ungrateful," "wicked," and "thoughtless." If this was what an artist's life had already fashioned of her, in heaven's name what would happen after she had had a taste of living in Paris!

Eduard recalled the innocent, sweet child whose portrait he had painted long ago, the wistful, graceful girl who had sat for him in the white gown she was to wear to the opera. Was it possible that that angel of a child had become this bold creature whom he had been commissioned to see? He shook his head. A memory also stirred of dark, passionate eyes, and a throbbing young voice exclaiming, "Don't tease, Uncle Eduard!"

Yes, it was the sweet, innocent ones with those sudden flare-ups one had to watch. He squared his shoulders and entered the building.

Clara's face lighted with pleasure when he appeared at her door. He kissed her ceremoniously on both cheeks.

"I was hoping you'd come, Uncle Eduard," she said. "In all Paris, there is no one I'd rather see at this moment than you."

Her ready smile, the enthusiastic ring in her voice, the sense of relief evident in her words puzzled him. So this, then, was Clara. She was up to his shoulders, a head of luxuriant black hair informally arranged, with loose wisps touching her cheeks. The same dark, lambent eyes, direct, yet mysterious, though at nineteen the fledgling look was gone.

He could not take his eyes off her as she took his coat and scarf. Obviously she must be hiding her true nature, if Wieck's description were accurate, under that still half-innocent girlish smile of hers. He decided to plunge in immediately before her charm made him forget the purpose of his visit.

"I ought to be scolding, not kissing you, Clara," he said with as much sternness as he could summon. "Since the day I had your father's letter warning me to be on the lookout for you, I must have aged five years. What do you mean by coming all this way to Paris without him? And what do you intend to do in *this* place?" He looked around her rooms suspiciously.

Was he serious? Was he teasing? Clara, too, had her memories. An impish, charming uncle, who faced the world with a gay heart. Eduard had changed in appearance, either time or care aging him in the intervening years. His cheeks were hollowed, his eyes protruded, his hair was graying. But she could not imagine his spirit ever growing old. No! That was ageless.

"I'm glad to know someone was worrying about me," she said, smiling brightly at him. "But, as you see, I'm perfectly safe. I'm not the little girl you last saw in Paris."

He took her hand and gave her a long, searching look. It was difficult to see in her face any evidence of her father's charges. "Take care, she will wrap you around her little finger," Wieck had warned him. "Be firm. Make her listen to reason. Send her home."

"I remember you well from those days, Clara," he said. "You were a golden girl, a loyal, sweet child. But what bad reports I get of you now!" He shook his head reprovingly.

Clara's smile died away. She withdrew her hand and stepped back from him. "I had hopes that we were going to be good friends, Uncle Eduard," she said. It was difficult to restrain the trembling that crept into her voice. The thought that her father had influenced him against her with "bad reports" wounded her deeply.

"But I *am* your friend," he insisted. "And believe me, Clara, in a city like Paris, you are going to need one. But are you entirely alone here? Where is that Frenchwoman your father spoke about?"

"I discharged her as soon as Henriette and I found this place. She was deceitful and of absolutely no value to me." Clara resented answering his questions now. Yet, since she had been in Paris (it was only a few days) she had more than once said to Henriette, "Wait! As soon as Uncle Eduard comes, we'll have no more difficulties."

Almost from the first hour of their arrival there had been trouble. Paris, they discovered, was smoldering as usual with political upheaval. There was continuous talk of uprisings. Emilie List, with whom they had spent their first night, and who gathered her news through her father's diplomatic channels, informed them that the "citizen king" had his agents constantly on the alert for spies, revolutionaries and especially foreign conspirators. Every piece of literature coming over the border was suspect. Clara had already had a taste of the king's censor. When she went to pick up the letters from Schumann for which she had been waiting so hungrily, a spruce little government clerk informed her that it would take three, possibly four weeks before she could have them. Indignantly she mentioned the names of numerous distinguished persons in Paris to whom she would appeal if he did not at once hand over her property. But the clerk, who was holding her precious packet between his fingers as he talked, told her to come back in a month with her passport. She left him defeated and in tears, her one hope resting on Uncle Eduard to help her unravel some of the red tape.

"Your situation here is worse than I thought," he was saying with a frown. "Not even a chaperone! Apparently you don't realize, Clara, what that means in Paris."

She was on the point of saying that he might be of service to her in that respect, but her pride restrained her. He must make the offer. She would not ask him.

"Who is Henriette?" he went on.

"A young girl I met in Stuttgart. She is my pupil and my companion. She's out just now on an errand."

"That won't do, Clara. Two young girls, living here alone. . . ."

"We'll manage," she said proudly. "Don't think, Uncle Eduard, that I am without friends. Herr List—"

"Herr List is not in Paris just now, your father informs me."

"But Emilie is here, and her parents will be back very soon. Pleyel and Erard are both expecting me. And Pauline Garcia lives just above us in this same *hôtel*."

At the moment, Pauline was the sensation of Paris. Sister to the almost legendary *Malibran*, whose superb voice and stormy, impulsive ways before her recent tragic death had attracted thousands in every capital of Europe, Pauline in her own right was capturing her audiences by the sheer magnetic quality of her operatic roles.

Eduard had heard her sing only the night before. Garcia was reputed to be carefully chaperoned, and surprisingly inexperienced in the ways of the world for a young girl who had followed her dramatic tenor father and prima donna sister into one wild adventure after another. Her proximity to Clara did not impress him as any guarantee of safety.

"Listen to me, *Liebchen*," he said. "Paris is no place for a woman alone. Take my advice. Turn about and go home. I beg you."

"Is that what Father instructed you to say?" Clara asked bitterly.

"He did. But I would have said it on my own. It's impossible for you to manage here by yourself. The French are hard to please. They're not exactly waiting for you with outstretched arms. To them, regardless of what the Empress of Austria or the Grand Duchess of Karlsruhe may think of you, you're just another foreign girl seeking to catch the public's ear. You'll get nowhere without your father, believe me."

"It wasn't I, Uncle Eduard, who asked him to stay behind."

"Perhaps not, but why ruin yourself because of pride? Do you think he doesn't know what is good for you? You can be sure this lover of yours isn't interested in Clara Wieck *the artist*. After you've run off with him, no one will have heard of you five years hence."

At that moment Henriette appeared, packages of groceries in her arms. Eduard looked inquisitively at the frail little figure, timidly passing them to deposit bundles on the kitchen table. Clara was far too angry to make an introduction.

"You've wasted your time and mine by coming here, Uncle Eduard," she said indignantly. "I know now how matters will stand between us. Tell Father anything you please. I will not turn about and go home. Oh, no! If he is concerned about my being 'a woman alone in Paris,' he knows very well how he could have avoided that."

"But, Clara—"

"Please go," she said, holding out his coat and scarf. "I'm dreadfully disappointed in you, Uncle Eduard."

He gave her a long, almost appealing look. As Wieck's ambassador, he had managed to make a mess of things. He wished now that he had stayed out of it altogether. "I only meant to help you, *Liebchen* . . . you see, your father wrote to me . . . he has so much at stake in you. He thinks . . ."

"He thinks I tremble without him," Clara interrupted angrily. "Well, tell him differently, Uncle Eduard. I'm grateful for what he has done for me in the past, but I can't go on living wholly for art as he wants me to. I have a mind of my own, and my own desires. No matter what anyone thinks, I intend to stay on in Paris and prove myself here. At Easter, a year from now, I will marry Robert Schumann and nothing will make me change my mind."

When he was gone, she sank down in a chair and covered her face with her hands. "Now, what shall I do, Henriette?" she said despairingly. "I really am alone!"

"I wouldn't worry about it, Clara," Henriette said solicitously. "You're a great artist. The public everywhere looks up to you. And if you appear now, without your father directing everything, you'll be admired all the more."

"It's more than just the concert," Clara said reflectively. "Who would have thought that in Paris, of all places, people would judge everything by externals. But already they're raising their hands above their heads when they hear that

not only do I not have my father with me, but not even a
mother or an aunt. Emilie says I ought at least to have 'an
old lady' when I go out into society, else I shan't be treated
with proper respect."

After a short silence, Henriette ventured cautiously, "Then,
perhaps you ought to send for your father after all—"

"No, no," Clara responded quickly. "I want him, but not
for anything will I beg. We shall just have to make the best
of things by ourselves, Henriette, and let the French think
what they please."

The following day, with March ninth set as a prospective
date for her first concert, she and Henriette began to make
their round of business calls. It soon appeared that every
aspiring pianist in Paris had announced concerts for the same
time. "Do they mean to frighten me out of it?" Clara asked
herself. "Well, I must have courage, regardless, and carry
through what I've begun." But a more helpful sign was that
both Pleyel and Erard, Paris' two famous piano dealers, offered
her free pianos on which to practice and perform. Her father
had written to both men criticizing her behavior and asking
their help in sending her home. But Erard, at least, was kind
enough to offer his salon for a concert and even volunteered
to help with all the arrangements.

So it was not a bad beginning after all. Clara's spirits
soared again. It took only a few days before she was going
about Paris quite boldly, determined as far as possible to live
the full artist's life. Accompanied by Henriette, she went
nightly to the opera, the theater or to concerts. She had the
thrill of hearing Pauline sing, and of meeting many famous
artists, Meyerbeer and Kalkbrenner among them. Chopin,
whom she longed to see again, was deathly ill, and in Mar-
seilles with George Sand. This she was told by Meyerbeer,

who proved to be most helpful to her in the way of suggestions. But nothing that she could recall as a "technique" of her father's was overlooked, for Clara quickly learned that in order to survive in this mecca she must develop shrewdness, a characteristic which was latent in her personality. With great poise, she made social calls on the Saxon Consul and the Austrian Ambassador, both visits resulting in the opening of important doors. It was no time at all before French and Russian ladies of the nobility were vying with one another for her services at their soirees.

At home she was happy in her close circle of young friends, Pauline Garcia, Henriette, and Emilie List. She wrote gaily to Schumann of their way of life together:

. . . A great deal is said about you here, if not to Emilie, then Henriette, and especially at the piano. Emilie, who has spent the night with us, and Henriette have commissioned me to write and tell you that I can cook a really excellent breakfast. They are now enjoying it. You have probably worried that I do not know how to cook. Be at ease about it. I shall learn soon enough when once I am with you. Emilie says: 'But you will only burn your piano-fingers!' What rubbish the two girls chatter to me about tea, coffee, and heaven knows what, with which I am told to amuse you, you poor fellow.

But her moment of greatest joy in Paris came on the twenty-fifth of February, when at last she received his letters. "I went shivering and shaking to the post with Emilie, presented my pass and got three letters!" she wrote to him. "I must have displayed my joy to the people in the post office. I could hardly speak. And what letters!"

The first made all her troubles seem worthwhile. What a pity she had not had it to cheer her during those fearsome coach journeys in Germany.

My beloved:—What am I in comparison with you? When I left Leipzig I thought I had experienced the worst. And you, a girl, gentle and delicately nurtured, for my sake are going alone into the great dangerous world. What you have now done is the greatest thing you have done for me.

I feel myself strengthened through and through. Some day you will be rewarded for your confidence and your independence. You are a wonderful girl, worthy of the highest reverence. When I wake at night and the wind and rain drive against my window and I think of you huddled up in the carriage with nothing but your art, so absolutely alone except perhaps that in your mind you are surrounded by beautiful pictures of the future, then my whole heart becomes softened and moved, and I do not know how I have deserved so much love.

To see such courage in one's betrothed gives one moral strength. In the last few days I have done work which would usually take me weeks. It was like the time when we became engaged in August '37. Everything pours out so easily. It is impossible to fail in anything. See! Such power have you given me, my Clara. Such a heroic girl must make her lover into something of a hero too.

Ah, Clara, how differently people love each other when they have to work and make sacrifices for one another.

Each word was like strong wine. It all went to her head and made her feel bigger than herself. In the next letter he said, "You must look at once like a madonna and a heroine!" His own experiences in Vienna, however, were not encouraging. Censors and competitors were blocking his efforts to reestablish his newspaper. More than this, he was now becoming doubtful as to the wisdom of making Vienna a center for the *Neue Zeitschrift*. "My conviction that no good paper can succeed here grows continually," he said, "and above all, no musical paper, for Vienna is entirely out of touch with central Germany." It was possible to read through the lines his homesickness for Leipzig, yet he pleaded with her to remain in Paris, always keeping in mind their goal of 1840:

Do not lose courage. You have been there only a few weeks. They will receive you without a boring old lady when once you make a beginning. Do not let your father come. Listen to me, I beg you. The old song and the old suffering would begin all over again. Now that you have got through the worst of it, the long journey, the first beginning and preliminaries in Paris, carry it through!

To "carry it through" Clara rose every morning at seven and seldom arrived home before midnight. Her debut at Erard's was a grand success. She heard herself called "the second Liszt," which was a source of great amusement to her and to Henriette. Each day she wrote to Schumann, filling her letters with little vignettes of her life in Paris.

. . . I played fairly well yesterday. Enclosed is a little flower from the bunch I wore in my dress. I received the bouquet from Emilie, but pretended it had come from you. I wore a black dress (they like that here), quite simple, a white camellia surrounded with small white flowers in my hair, and among the flowers the Empress of Austria's brooch. Do you smile at my childish description? Ah, but I know you would have liked me. I looked quite imposing.

.   .   .   .

I dined with Meyerbeer the other day, and met Heine and Jules Janin there. Heine speaks bitterly of Germany. He is coming to see me before long.

.   .   .   .

You did not suspect that I was still sitting at the piano at two o'clock this morning playing your *Carnaval*, did you? I was at a certain Countess Perthuis' and all the connoisseurs stayed behind. No one will listen to Bach fugues here, not even the connoisseurs.

.   .   .   .

I got through my concert yesterday quite successfully. I wished you had been there. I created a genuine sensation, such as no artist has produced for many a day. It was extremely full, but the expenses are so great in Paris that there cannot be anything left over, and indeed, I expected nothing else. My name is made. That is enough for me.

.   .   .   .

Today at Bertin's I met Berlioz. I did not know it was he at first, and wondered who it was that kept talking about you. He is quiet, has extraordinary thick hair, and always looks on the ground, always keeps his eyes down. Tomorrow he is coming to see me . . . his new opera has not taken at all.

He rewarded her efforts and enthusiasm with news of his own creative ventures:

I have not written you for a week, but I have reveled in the thought of you and have loved you as I never did before. I sat at the piano all the week and composed and wrote and laughed and cried all at once. You will find all this fairly depicted in my Op. 20, the great *Humoreske*, which is already being printed. See how quickly things go with me! Invented, written down, printed. And this is how I like it. Twelve sheets finished in eight days. Now you forgive me, don't you, for making you wait a little. . . .

Thus, in their separation, they went on giving inspiration to one another, full of dreams of the future. Yet there was something pulling at Clara's heart all the while, which, oddly enough, increased the greater her success in Paris became. She missed her father. She longed for lessons from him again, finding it difficult to be her own musical critic. More, she was conscious of a growing sympathy for him, unaware that he was carefully building this up by maneuvers of his own. Toward the end of April, she told Schumann: "Surely Father must often feel very unhappy. He is to be pitied, and I often grieve over it in my heart. But I cannot possibly alter it at all. Some day it will be said that I have brought him to the grave, but One above will forgive me. Have I not fulfilled all my duty toward him? Ah, Robert, forgive me if sometimes a sudden melancholy comes over me when I think of my father. It is so sad."

The "sudden melancholy" was not as spontaneous as she imagined. Her father had begun to write to her again, long, newsy letters, carefully avoiding mention of the cause of their estrangement. But at the same time he was sending a different kind of letter to Emilie, which Emilie in turn gave to Clara to read. These gave a truly heart-rending picture of himself as having been "thrown over" by his daughter after many long years of service to her. It was "the old song and the old suffering" of which Schumann had warned, but Clara had no objective view of her father. The letters gradually began to turn Emilie's head. Despite all that had happened, she soon became Wieck's partisan. He was appealing to her, as the wiser and more sophisticated of the two girls, to be influential with Clara. He spoke of Clara's being "poor" should she marry Schumann, and convinced her that he only had Clara's best interests at heart. Emilie had never known privation. The very thought of being "poor" made her shudder. She began to look on Clara's romance with a more practical eye.

One night when Pauline and Henriette too were present,

she brought up the subject for discussion with Clara. Why, she asked her, was she anxious to be married so soon, just when her fame was at its peak and Schumann had not yet made his fortune. "It seems a pity," she said, unaware that she was catching Clara at a time of weak resistance.

"Do you really think, Emilie, that I am acting impulsively? Ought I to urge Father to come, and put Robert off a little longer?"

Emilie nodded. "What harm can come of it? You've done well without your father, but think how much better and smoother things will run with him. You want to go to England, perhaps to Holland next winter. It's impossible to travel that great distance without a man. As for Schumann, I know he has tried, but he's hardly begun to make a name for himself. He has nothing to offer you yet. Meanwhile, you can increase your own fortune while you give him more time. Here is another letter from your father. Read it. Does he say anything which does not make good sense?"

Clara read the letter and was in tears when she put it aside.

"What do you think, Pauline?" she asked of the young singer. Pauline was in love with a journalist who was a great deal older than herself and who lived in Italy. She had not seen him for a long time.

"I don't agree with Emilie at all," she said forcefully. "This year, next year, and the year after that, Clara, these same arguments will still sound valid if you want them to. 'Your fame is at its peak.' What does that matter? How many times will you be told that when you want to do something other than perform? Besides, you've sworn a dozen times to Schumann not to put him off any longer. Believe me, if I had my chance, I'd marry this very day! Oh, how I should like to see anyone stop me."

"And you, Henriette?" Clara asked.

Henriette, thinking of her father with whom she had the warmest relationship, answered thoughtfully, "I wouldn't want to lose my father if there were a way to avoid it. It seems to me that, since you've proved to him how strong you are, that you really mean to do without him unless he recognizes your right to love whom you please, he will treat you differently now. I agree with Emilie. What harm can come of bringing him to Paris?"

Emilie and Henriette were giving Clara the answers she wanted. Pauline was her conscience. But she closed her ears against the latter, and that very night, with a greatly agitated heart, sent off a long letter to her father. In it she reaffirmed her passionate love for Schumann, but at the same time offered a compromise. If he would consent to her marriage as soon as Schumann showed an income of one thousand *Thaler*, she would solemnly promise not to marry "until we have the prospect of a life untrammeled by care." The letter was covered with tears. "Ah, Father," she wrote, "you think I am not good. You say that my character is spoiled, that I do not know how you love me, that I am ungrateful. In this you do me a serious wrong. Emilie and Henriette are witnesses with what love I always speak of you, even after your reproachful letters. Often have I wept by myself at being parted from you. . . ."

Was it a step backward, a blunder from which she could never recover? Clara hardly took time to think. Indeed, in her anxiety to make the reconciliation permanent, without first waiting for an answer from her father, she quickly sent off another letter, this one to Schumann. It was a letter which might well have put an end to him, but, as matters turned out, was destined to be the decisive turning point in both their affairs.

Paris, May 2, 1838:

My most dearly beloved Robert: It is with a heavy heart that I set out to write to you today. I must tell you of what has long been struggling within me and has today come to a head. It concerns the happiness of us both. We cannot be married next Easter, we should not be happy. Let me speak to you quite frankly, my beloved Robert. Our happiness would be troubled in two directions, first on account of the uncertainty of our future, and then on account of my father. I shall make Father most unhappy if I marry you without having an assured future in view. Trouble about me would bring him to the grave and it would be my fault. . . . From what I know of you, I am sure that you would be most unhappy if you had even on one single occasion to worry about our livelihood. As artists we should both perish, overwhelmed with cares. All this came before me so vividly, that at last I could endure it no longer, I had to share it with you, and I spoke to Emilie about it, who thought me right, and you, Robert, are sure to understand. I have written to Father to ask if he will give his consent when you can show him an income of 1000 *Thaler.* I, on my side, will promise him to enter upon no alliance with you unless we look forward to days free from anxiety. I had to do it! But I also told him that I would never give you up, I could never love again, and I once more assure you of this. Never will I give you up, never will I cease to be your faithful Clara. Ah! What a battle I fought before I decided to write to you this time, to tear you away from your fairest hopes, but I could no longer bear this thought by myself. You are a man, Robert, are you not, and will not abandon yourself to too deep sorrow. . . . Father means to come here this summer, and then to go with me to Belgium, Holland, England, etc. I realize that I can do much more with him than alone; not that my courage fails me at all, oh! no, I had made up my mind to undertake all these journeys alone, but from the start one is thought more of everywhere if one is accompanied by a man. His letter to Emilie was desperate and heart-rending and it caused the sudden ripening into decision of an idea which I had long been turning over in my mind. I wrote a letter to him, and if that does not soften him, I do not know what more I can say. I will let you know his answer at once, but I beg you too, my good Robert, not to let me live long in this fearful suspense. I kiss you in most heartfelt unalterable love, Your faithful Clara.

THIRTY-ONE

THE STARS were pale that spring night, holding back their fire. Loneliness in shadows crept at his heels.

"You are a man, are you not, Robert, and will not abandon yourself to deep sorrow?"

Slowly Schumann made his way across the deserted square and down an avenue of lindens. Earlier there had been the wild frivolity of the festival crowd, Viennese lights and Viennese voices to mock him. Now, in the midnight stillness, it was Clara's words alone, clear as the beat of a drum: you are a man, are you not, you are a man . . .

Digging his fists into his pockets, he increased his pace, plunging steadily onward, as if he wished the horizon, engulfed in darkness, could enfold him forever. The Danube, never still, never silent, churned a melancholy cadence in the soft black wind. Schumann followed its course until he could follow it no longer. Then he climbed the hills above the sleeping valley and turned his eyes skyward looking for the dawn.

By now, his grief was gone, replaced by that which he abhorred most in the world: hatred and anger. He recalled almost word for word what he had said to Clara once before when Wieck, with his cunning, had momentarily wooed her away from him.

I do not know what to say about your having once more come to an understanding with your father. You are, pardon me, like a couple of children together. You cry, he rages, and then it all goes back to what it was before and we never get any further. You, with your good heart, stand midway between us. But it will not be possible for you to belong to him and to me at the same time. You must give up one: him or me.

Him or me—Schumann saw Wieck's face burning before him as clearly as the moon, and with a sudden violent gesture, shook his fist at the weird mirage.

"Be damned!" he shouted aloud. "Be damned!"

But he was trembling at the hammer of hatred beating in his brain. Beads of perspiration ran down his face. The loss of gentleness always made him ill. Still, he was done forever with running. Done with turning the other cheek. Done, too, with the fears and whims and foolishness of Clara. He loved her. He would have her. But on his own terms now.

How dare she speak to him of "a man." Was it less than a man who, out of the deepest anguish for her, had conceived *Fantasia?* Was it less than a man who, in the throes of love, had created *Kreisleriana* and *Novelletten?* What an insult was her question!

But then, perhaps a man ought to be something else. Perhaps, instead of turning sorrow into glory, he should tear across the hills, beat down his opponent with his fists, grab up his prize and cry aloud to the world: What is mine is mine! Perhaps that was the kind of man needed for this battle. Wieck's kind of man.

Though I grow sick to my soul of it, he determined, I will face him with new weapons. Whatever it takes to win— whatever I have to do—from this moment on *I* will be the aggressor.

Exhausted, he turned and descended the hill. All around him was the dawn brilliant with streaks of fire. He had watched it come, cutting the black cape from the sky, swiftly, and without pity.

Later that same day, Schumann visited the office of an acquaintance in Vienna, a lawyer named Hermann. He related his story quite candidly, not omitting Clara's many vacillations. His eyes were burning from fatigue. His voice too was affected; one moment he was hoarse, the next unable to speak above a whisper. To Hermann, he hardly seemed in a state of health to begin the long court battle for which he was asking. The intensity with which this love affair had affected Schumann physically and mentally was more than obvious.

"Are you certain you want to go through with this?" Hermann asked. "Quite aside from the strain, what guarantee have you of Clara's full support? An action of this kind against her father is a severe test. How do you know she will see it through to the end?"

"I know her," Schumann said wearily. "She'll come around to me again after the letter I sent her this morning. I made my position clear. I spared her nothing. She chooses now between Wieck and me for the last time."

"But are you absolutely certain . . ."

"That she will choose me?" Schumann anticipated him. "She can't help herself. Too much has passed between us. I've been a fool to have waited this long."

"Then you're determined to force the issue. Think carefully, Schumann. It means a trial, perhaps a painful one, exposing everything to the public eye."

"It can't be helped," Schumann replied somberly. "Let the world judge who has been sinned against. I don't intend to give up until I have Clara with me once and for all."

Two hours later, Schumann emerged from Hermann's office carrying with him two documents, one a formal letter to Wieck asking for a consent to the marriage, the other a petition addressed to the Leipzig Court of Appeals in the event of another refusal.

The letter to Wieck was cold and to the point:

Once more I come before you, hand in hand with Clara, to beg your consent to our marriage next Easter. Two years have passed since my first proposal. You doubted if we should remain true to each other. We have done so. Nothing can make us waver in our belief in our future happiness.

What I wrote to you once before concerning my income was absolutely true. Indeed everything has turned out even more favorably and securely. We can look forward to the future with confidence. Listen to the voice of nature. Do not drive us to extremes. Soon it will be Clara's twentieth birthday. Give peace on that day. Say yes. We need rest after so terrible a strife. You owe it to Clara and to me. I look forward with longing to your definite answer.

Schumann posted it at once, having the fullest confidence that Clara was already bitterly regretting her momentary act of cowardice. His letter to her, full of stinging rebuke, would doubtless cause many angry tears, but in the end she would submit quietly, admitting the justice of his position, for hers was defenseless.

And he was right. She yielded almost at once.

"Tell me, my good, beloved Robert, what am I to do in order to awaken once more your tender feelings toward me? Please tell me! I cannot be at ease when I know you are angry with me." She signed this letter: "Your faithful sweetheart, before long, your happy wife."

Schumann was quick to forgive her and return to his old tone of tenderness, but he wasted no time in telling her what

she "must do." He immediately sent her a draft of the court
petition and a copy of the letter he had sent to her father.
"Think these documents over carefully," he told her. "They
are the most important letters of our whole lives."

While awaiting word from Wieck, Schumann then prepared the next phase of his offensive. He made ready to leave
Vienna. His exile was over. He was going home. But one
word of advice given him by Hermann he was anxious to carry
through almost immediately. This was to pay a visit to Clara's
mother in Berlin.

"If Frau Bargiel approves of you and gives you her written
consent to the marriage, this may prove acceptable to the
court in place of the father's. At any rate, it's worth a try,"
Hermann said. "Remember that when Wieck realizes what
you're up to, he'll move heaven and earth to harm you. So
by all means, if you can accomplish it, bring Frau Bargiel
into court on your behalf."

Despite his urgent desire to get back to Germany, it was
not without some regret that Schumann walked the streets
of Vienna for the last time. Vienna! "With its tower of
St. Stephen, its countless watery ribbons." The land of Beethoven, Schubert and Haydn! Often he thought how they,
too, must have gazed on the city, taking in the majesty of the
distant Alps, following the course of the Danube, looking up
to the tower shaking their heads at its dizzy height.

When the charming, living landscape stands before us,
What chords will vibrate that never resounded within us before!

For him, this prediction had come true. How many new
and brave compositions had been written here, most of them
with a steel pen he had found one day on Beethoven's grave.
It was as though the genius of the master flowed through with
the ink, lending him inspiration, strengthening his own genius,

urging him to write on and on, one splendid song after another! And he had been fortunate, also, to discover a treasure other than his own for the world to hear.

Many a young musician, [he told his *Neue Zeitschrift* readers,] after the first few days of excitement in Vienna, has probably wandered, as I have, to the Wahringer Cemetery, there to lay his gift of flowers, even were it but a wild rosebush such as I found on Beethoven's grave. Franz Schubert's resting place was undecorated. At last! One warm desire of my life was fulfilled. I gazed long at those sacred graves, almost envying the one buried between them, a certain Earl O'Donnell if I am not mistaken.

Then, on my way home, I remembered that Schubert's brother, Ferdinand, to whom he had been much attached, was still living. I sought him out and discovered that he bore a strong resemblance to the bust that stands beside Schubert's grave, shorter than Franz, but strongly built, with a face expressive of honesty as well as musical ability. He had heard of me from that veneration for his brother I so often publicly professed and allowed me to see the treasures of Schubert's composition which were still in his possession. The sight of this hoard of riches thrilled me with joy! Where to begin? Where to leave off? Among other things were several symphonies, many of which have never yet been heard. Who knows how long the symphony of which I now speak might not have lain buried in dust and darkness had I not at once arranged with Ferdinand Schubert to send it immediately to the directing artist of the Gewandhaus Concerts in Leipzig, Mendelssohn himself, whose fine glance perceives even the most timid of new budding beauties, and necessarily, therefore, the dazzling splendors of masterly perfection. . . .

The "dazzling splendor" which he had rescued from oblivion that fateful day was Franz Schubert's immortal *C major Symphony!* If he had accomplished nothing more than this during his Vienna exile, Schumann thought, his time would not have been spent in vain.

282   SONG WITHOUT END

Meanwhile in Paris the musical season was drawing to a close. In the middle of June, Clara and Henriette moved to the country, to Bougival, where Clara was living "as a hermit," as she told Schumann, "and for whole days never seeing a single soul from the outside." It was a time of deep reflection for her, for she was conscious of a decisive change in Schumann; indeed she was fairly reeling from it. After her first sad siege, when his furious letter (which she immediately destroyed, more out of shame than anger) had led her to think that he might never forgive her, she recuperated quickly, secretly relieved that choice and decision were entirely out of her hands, and that it was he who was taking the offensive. He was right not to trust her longer. How often had she proved indecisive! How easily she wavered between these two powerful poles in her life! Better that Robert, if he wanted her, pursue her in all haste, barely giving her time to catch her breath. And he was doing just that.

In July came a letter from her mother in Berlin. "My beloved Clara, your Robert has been here since yesterday and I can tell you, to my real joy, that I approve of your choice, and that I grow fonder of him every hour. The first and most necessary thing, my dear child, is that you should come here. Without your presence in person, there can be no possible end to this affair. . . . I have written to your father, but he has not answered. However, that cannot be helped; matters must be brought to an end. If I had you here now, how happy it would make me to see you both with me. Robert played several of his compositions to us today which gave us the highest enjoyment! What a beautiful talent! How happy I shall be in your marriage!"

Robert's letter, written on the same day, described his joyful meeting with Marianne. "Yesterday I was with her nearly all day. We talked of nothing but you. I quite love her, with her (your) eyes, and I can never tear myself away from her."

But Clara hesitated to go to them, much as she wanted to. It seemed to her wrong to do anything which would stir her father to even greater anger than he must be feeling at this moment with a court case pending against him. Daughter against father! How sad that was.

Still, it could not be helped. His reply to Schumann's letter of proposal was a "consent" so outrageous in its terms and its thinly veiled slanders that she knew there was no longer any hope, no other course left open but to proceed against him. "I have not subscribed to your conditions and I tell you I will never subscribe to them," she wrote him angrily. He had sent her a paper to sign in which she was to agree that she and Schumann leave Saxony, never to return as long as he (Wieck) was alive. She was to give up all her property and all claim to her inheritance. Schumann must submit a formally audited statement of income to a lawyer of Wieck's choosing, and never, either by word of mouth or in writing, communicate with him unless he expressly asked for it.

"I have too much proper pride," Clara stormed back. "How could you think I would agree to sign a paper in which evil things are said of the man I love? You are not serious, and even if you were, I can only say, 'You will never get me to do such a thing.'"

Instead she immediately put her signature under Schumann's name on the court petition, and forwarded it to her lawyer in Leipzig, asking him to process it with all possible speed.

There was something almost plaintively sad in that brief document which Schumann, with Hermann's aid, had drawn up.

We, the undersigned, have for a long time cherished a common and heartfelt wish to be united to each other in matrimony. But up to the present time there has been an obstacle to the fulfillment of this determination, whose removal is necessary for the attainment of our object, though it gives us the deepest pain to seek to obtain it in this manner. That is to say, the father of the co-signatory, Clara Wieck, regardless of repeated requests which have been courteously made to him, refuses us his consent. We cannot explain the grounds of his refusal; we are conscious of no faults. Our circumstances are such that we can venture to look forward to an assured future. The cause, therefore, which prevents Herr Wieck from giving his consent to this union can only be a feeling of personal animosity toward the other signatory, who yet believed that he on his side had fulfilled every duty which a man owes to the father of her whom he has chosen to be his companion through life. However this may be, we are not willing to give up our carefully weighed determination on this account, and therefore we approach the High Court with the most humble request:

That your worships will cause Herr Wieck to give his consent to our union in marriage, or if you think fit, would graciously be pleased to give us your consent instead of his. Nothing but the conviction of the urgent necessity of this step can reconcile us to it, and we are at the same time animated by the confident hope that in this case, as in so many others, time will heal this painful division.

                              Robert Schumann
                              Clara Wieck (at present in Paris)

"I wrote my name firmly and resolutely and with boundless happiness," Clara informed Schumann. She now had only one burning ambition: to make up to him for all that he had suffered, to be his faithful comrade through life, to manage their lives so that he could live wholly for music, for its own sake, and that no further anxiety trouble the beauty of his life as an artist.

Clara's long struggle with herself was over.

THIRTY-TWO

A LIGHT SNOW had fallen in the morning, brushed everything with the thinnest coat of white, and then the wind, which was gusty, swept it all away. A little crowd, made up in the main of students and very young boys, who wore mufflers to protect their ears from the December cold, stood outside the music master's house waiting eagerly for him to emerge.

"Ah, he won't come out this time any more than he did the last," said one young man with a look of disappointment.

His companion, whose nose was already beet-red from the cold, nudged him with a suggestive smile. "But he had better, hey? If he doesn't, things are likely to go against him, and he won't like that—not him! It's 'now or never,' the judges say."

They were referring to the two previous occasions on which Wieck, for reasons of his own, had shrewdly ignored a summons to appear before the Court of Appeals for a hearing on his daughter's petition. These delaying tactics, forcing postponement of the trial, had been the cause of much disappointment, not only to Clara who, because she now lived with Marianne, was made to travel back and forth between Berlin and Leipzig, but to the public, which followed each new development in the Wieck-Schumann feud with bated breath.

Wieck himself had deliberately provoked the affair into an open scandal, allowing rumours of the charges he intended to bring against Schumann to leak into every respectable home in Leipzig. Now the day of climax was come, the day when he must openly stand up in court and say these insulting things to the young composer's face. The curious had come to follow him to the hearing, to see with their own eyes the vindictive old professor who once had doted on his daughter but now seemed bent on destroying her. What a far cry from those other times when spectators gathered to watch the two set off on tour, the father visibly proud of the loving young girl who clung to his arm.

To the delight of the onlookers, Wieck did not disappoint them this time. He soon came out of the house, followed by Clementine who was securely wrapped in furs. Quickly the little group made a path through which the two passed without once looking to left or to right. As the courthouse was but a short distance away, Wieck had apparently decided to walk. He moved along with a brisk step, the upward turn of his lips betraying a hungry anticipation for the event to come. But not so Clementine who went forward more slowly.

Her life had been one long misery since the quarrel had begun. People in the town had their definite sympathies in the case, and she was not blind to the fact that only in her husband's presence did anyone pretend to side with him. She herself was openly snubbed on the streets. As for Schumann, he had a multitude of friends. His landlady, his roommate, his colleagues, even the numerous shopkeepers with whom he was acquainted, all took his battle onto their own shoulders. She as well as Wieck had become the victim of their hatred. If only her husband would let Clara go! How many times did she say it to herself, Let her go! Let her go! There was not a day's peace! Clara's brothers were become like strangers. Her own two girls (she had borne a second child) heard daily reproaches of the missing Clara, and did not know what to think of their older sister. Marie, being groomed to take Clara's place as a piano virtuoso, was lately the victim of nervous strain. It was with genuine longing that Clementine recalled the early days when her home had had its share of friendship and love. She knew now that she had gained nothing from having sided with her husband against Clara. The girl was more a fixation with Wieck than ever. He thought of nothing else but of possible ways to delay or prevent her marriage.

At the threshold of their destination, Wieck paused and spoke to her. "Unless I give you the word," he warned her, "say nothing." She nodded, looked around with uneasy eyes, and followed after him into the building. They were the last of the principals to enter the small room assigned for the hearing. All eyes turned upon them, and upon Wieck especially, as with his usual bulldog look, he confidently strode forward and took his seat.

Clara, who was sitting next to Schumann, felt her mouth quiver during that tense interval of silence in which her father was the subject of such keen attention. If only he would look at her! If only by some sign, a kind look, he would indicate his willingness to concede! Was it possible he would permit this terrible farce to go on? She felt as if she might faint. Her mouth went dry. Sensing her emotion, Schumann caught her hand inside his own and held it tightly. "Steady, Clara," she heard him whisper. She nodded to him wordlessly, squared her shoulders, and resolutely turned her eyes away from her father's immobile face. Not once had he looked in her direction.

The hearing began promptly with a clerk reading aloud the petition she and Schumann had submitted. Not a movement, not a sound from the listeners throughout, yet the room was vibrating with the varied emotions. Clara was thinking of the heartbreaking day four months ago when she had returned to Leipzig from Paris, unable to go "home" to the house where she had been so lovingly brought up, the doors of which were now forever closed to her. As the carriage passed it by, and she saw from a little way off the tightly closed shutters of her room, it needed much restraint for her not to get out, run to the door, and beg to see her childhood possessions for the last time. Only the warm welcome she received from Frau Carl, a sister of her mother's with whom she took refuge, and Marianne's arrival the following day, was able to make up to her for that lonely, distressing moment.

Schumann, with ashen face, was reliving the torture he had been made to endure as a result of Wieck's infamous slanders. One day recently a group of schoolboys running at his heels had shouted insulting jibes, laughing, and pointing their fingers at him. What agony of soul he had suffered. What a test by fire Wieck had put him through! He shuddered at the thought that the vicious man's victory might come, not today, but at some future time when the consequences of such terrible mental suffering might take its toll. He intended to sue Wieck for these outrages, but he knew that the scars on his mind could not be effaced through retaliation. Perhaps Clara's love, possession of her from whom he derived so much power, could cure him in time. Perhaps—! It was on this that Schumann was thinking as the clerk read aloud from their petition.

The reading was over. There was a rustling in the court-room, an air of suspense. Friends, neighbors, strangers leaned forward awaiting the first words from the President of the Court. Many had come from Dresden. Ernst Becker was there from Freiburg. Emilie List from Paris. All had their own thoughts, the strangers of the gossip which had begun as far back as when Wieck first took Clara to Paris, ignoring the dangers of cholera; the neighbors of Clementine's long-time jealousy of her famous stepdaughter; friends of their own small part in shaping the destiny of Robert and Clara.

The president, impressive in his black robe, cleared his throat. He too was not entirely unaffected by this case, since he was an old acquaintance of the music master. "Herr Wieck," he said in a quiet, almost informal tone, "in matters of this kind, we of the court are always hopeful that some reconciliation will have taken place between the parties concerned. Was not that your hope, too, sir?"

Now, for the first time, Wieck looked fixedly at Clara. "It was—it is," he said, with an affected sigh, "but when a daughter, to whom one has given most of his life, rejects every reasonable offer, well, then, there is little hope . . ."

"Am I to understand by that, sir, that you, for your part, sincerely wish to resolve the matter peacefully, that along the lines of your present thinking, the petition which was just read no longer needs to be a serious concern of this body?"

Wieck stood up, blinked rapidly, then made his reply in a slow, deliberative tone. "Sir! I consider that petition a most evil document, drawn up for the most evil of purposes! It is obviously meant to lure an innocent, young girl . . ."

"One moment, Herr Wieck! If you please!" said the president, interrupting him. "The court asks for a simple answer. Are you prepared now to withdraw your previous objections and permit the cosignatories of this petition, Robert Schumann and Clara Wieck, to be wed as they so desire?"

"Oh, let her go, Friedrich! Let her go!" Clementine pleaded in a low whisper.

Wieck, growing red in the face, ignored her. He reached into his pocket and dug out a fistful of papers which he shook wildly in the air. "Here! Here," he shouted, "are ample pieces of evidence to show why . . ."

Once again the president rapped loudly on the table. "Your answer, Herr Wieck. Say 'yes' or 'no.' "

Wieck turned slowly and looked at Schumann. As of old, his pupils dilated, and splotches of purple appeared on his cheeks. His voice, charged with invective, fairly exploded in the room.

"No!" he hissed. "That is my answer—now and forever. No! I am a man of honor, sir. Can I stand by without a word and see my daughter debased by a scoundrel, a liar, an incompetent and immoral man?"

Murmurs of angry protest rose from Schumann's many friends in the room. The president, who was now prepared for the worst, motioned for quiet. "I must ask you to restrain yourself, Herr Wieck," he said sternly. "You will have full opportunity later in this hearing to state the reasons for your disapproval."

Wieck sat down and Schumann's lawyer, Einert, took the floor. After the previous dramatics, his presentation (which was as Schumann wished it) was simple and dignified, making no effort at retaliation. He began by submitting a financial statement to prove Schumann's ability to support a wife. It read as follows:

1. In government bonds......... 1000 *Thaler*
2. From Schumann and Sons.... 7540   "
3. Inheritance.................. 1500   "
4. Sales of music............... 100   "
5. Earnings from compositions.. 100   "
6. Other sources............... 624   "

The total, over ten thousand *Thaler*, far exceeded Wieck's demand of a thousand *Thaler*. Clara's dowry, and her earnings from four long years of traveling, could not be included, as Wieck was spitefully keeping it from her. She no longer even had the money with which to buy her trousseau. Einert concluded his brief remarks by reading a few glowing testimonials of Schumann's character and of his musical gift, all predicting bright prospects for his future. His former teachers, Kuntzsch and Dorn, as well as Franz Liszt and Felix Mendelssohn, were among those who lent their support.

But to these last words from Einert, the judges listened unmoved. It was clear to everyone that such tributes meant less to them than the statement of Schumann's modest income. Had the two hundred *Thaler* earned from his "art" been all that he could show, his case would have been dismissed at once. Saxon judges were business-minded men, not given to sentiment. An "artist," no matter how gifted, if he were in straitened circumstances, meant no more to them than did the poor workmen of Bavaria who were restrained by law from marrying until they could prove themselves to be owners of considerable property. In Saxony, where the marriage laws were more liberal, if the father's consent was lacking, the court, as a last resource, might give its approval, but only after the most careful deliberation on the prospective bridegroom's circumstances. It was for this reason that Einert was careful to put his greatest stress on Schumann as a man of means.

Wieck knew that he could not defeat Schumann in the face of such figures, and altered his tactics accordingly. He took over the courtroom like a bull entering the arena, his nostrils, his eyes, his half-cocked head drawing all eyes in wonderment as he plunged into his vitriolic attack. Schumann, sitting pale and silent throughout, was impaled without mercy, forced to watch his physical weaknesses imitated and mocked, his soft voice put to ridicule, his manhood challenged. He heard, as if in a dream, Wieck accuse him of moral laxness in words that did not fail to satisfy the sensation seekers, and it was none other than Carl Banck who was quoted as an authority on his character!

Half-rising in her chair, outraged by the whole proceeding, Clara was about to cry out in protest, but Einert, as well as Schumann, restrained her.

"He is making a spectacle of himself," Einert assured her. "Everyone knows why Banck hates Schumann. Everyone knows all these charges to be malicious and false. . . ."

Wieck's first intention had been to ruin Schumann through Ernestine, from whom he was positive he would have incontestable evidence of Schumann's bad faith and immorality. But Ernestine, now the Countess Zedwitz, refused to join him in his game. She side-stepped his request for cooperation with this short, simple reply:

How is my good Clara? I have read so much about her in the papers, and you may be sure that it has brought great pleasure to me and my family. Clara will never be happy without Schumann. She told me so herself, and I know that she loves him beyond words.

Left, then, only with Banck's help, which was more than willingly given, Wieck swiftly changed his emphasis, delving into Schumann's student days for stories of irresponsibility in debt, excessive drinking of beer, and general instability of character. For some reason, he leaned most heavily on the drinking. Knowing how to put on a good scene, he exaggerated, gesticulated, and shouted as he recounted "eye-witness proof" of Schumann reeling along Leipzig streets in a highly intoxicated condition. And this was the man to whom he was expected to give approval for marriage to his daughter? Never!

"He was most passionate, so that the President of the Court

had to call him to order," Clara recorded in her diary that same night, "and each time it cut me to the heart. I could hardly bear that he should have to experience this humiliation. He looked at me with terrible anger, but he only once said anything against me. I would so gladly have once more entreated him, there, before the court, but I was afraid that he might thrust me from him. *This day has separated us forever*, or at least has torn to pieces the tender bond between father and child. My heart too feels as if it were torn to pieces! Robert behaved very well with all his characteristic self-possession which was the best thing he could do in the face of such passion. I only love him the more now that he has had to allow himself to be publicly insulted for my sake."

Decision on the case was set aside for January fourth, an almost intolerable three weeks to wait. Despite Wieck's clever display of fireworks to cover his flimsy testimony, Einert was confident of victory. "I am no wizard," he told Schumann as they left the courtroom together. "But I think I can safely predict that this love story of yours is going to have a happy ending. You will have your wedding as planned, by Easter."

But it was not destined to be so. Easter passed them by. There was no wedding to celebrate. To everyone's surprise Wieck had come off with a temporary victory. With his uncanny grasp of what "a good show" meant in the courtroom, the wily old man had actually succeeded in impressing the authorities with at least one of his arguments. Before giving its approval, the court demanded of Schumann that he come forward with proof that he was not, as Wieck had charged, "addicted to strong drink."

Though this proof was quickly forthcoming, with all of Schumann's colleagues standing by him to a man, it meant for him and for Clara another heartbreaking postponement.

Months went by. The suit dragged on and on, the court keeping them in agonizing suspense with repeated delays of its final decision. During this long wait, Clara attempted to enhance her own feeble fortune by numerous short tours on which she was always accompanied by Marianne. Wieck did not leave her alone for a moment. He plagued her with anonymous letters, tantalizing but always false propositions for ending the quarrel, and the circulation of a new, scandalous document to injure her name, and especially Schumann's, in the various cities in which she appeared to give her concerts. There seemed to be no end to his rascality.

Schumann, meanwhile, though he was more productive than ever, occupying himself with completing a cycle of songs set to Heine's poems, and outlining numerous other ambitious musical projects, could not put out of his mind all these fresh assaults on his character. "You may think that you will be able to reconcile me to your father later on," he warned Clara, "but give up all hope of that. The faintest wish of this kind on your part would be an insult to me. Make up your mind on this point, Clara, which otherwise may endanger our happiness. You see—I have been betrayed into an angry tone, when angry words and angry people are an abomination to me. . . ."

At long last, however, the duel of wills came to an end. On the first of August, 1840 Schumann was given full clearance by the court, while Wieck was informed that he had ten days in which to appeal. "Heaven grant that he may leave it alone!" Clara wrote in her diary.

They waited. They held their breaths. The silence was almost more frightening than the noise, and then, it was all over. The tenth day came and went—Wieck had indeed "let it alone." Was it because in another month Clara would reach her twenty-first birthday? Had he sucked out his last, bitter drop of vengeance? Whatever the reason, he drew in his horns and sulked behind closed doors. Nevertheless, the cautious young lovers went about their wedding plans in secret. They decided to be married on the eve of Clara's birthday. Marianne, not her father, would be at her side.

Clara's diary, faithfully kept all during this period, records her last day as Clara Wieck, her first as Clara Schumann:

September 11th: Polterabend! [wedding eve]. My Robert has given me a beautiful bridal gift, *Myrtles.* [The copy was printed in gold with the dedication, "To my beloved Clara on the eve of our wedding from her Robert."] I was quite overcome! Some friends spent a merry evening with us.

September 12th: What am I to say about this day! The wedding took place at ten o'clock in Schönefeld [near Leipzig] beginning with a choral. Then the minister gave a short and simple address, but one which spoke from the heart to the heart. My own heart was filled with thankfulness to Him who had at last led us across so many rocks and cliffs to each other. . . . It was a beautiful day, and even the sun which had hidden itself for many days past poured its mild rays upon us as we drove to the wedding, as if it wished to bless our union. Nothing disturbed me on this day, and it shall be inscribed in this book as the happiest and most important day of my life. One part of my life is now ended; if I have known much trouble in my youth, I have also known much joy. I will never forget that. Now a new life is beginning, a beautiful life, a life in him whom I love above all, above myself. But grave duties rest with me too. Heaven lend me strength to fulfill them faithfully like a good wife. . . .

The confidence with which she and Robert took their vows was shared by all who came that day to witness and many from afar who loved them well. One of these, Franz Liszt, took it upon himself to express the sentiment of all their friends, a bright and unerring prophecy: *In the world of art, no happier or more harmonious combination could be imagined than that of the creative man with the interpretive wife. The annals of art will in no way separate the memories of these two, nor be able to utter their names apart from one another. The future will weave a golden shimmer about both their heads and allow to shine over both brows but one single star.*

BIBLIOGRAPHY

BIBLIOGRAPHY

Abraham, Gerald (ed.). *Schumann, a Symposium.* New York: Oxford University Press, 1952.

Barzun, Jacques. *Berlioz and His Century, an Introduction to the Age of Romanticism.* Boston: Little, Brown & Company, 1950.

Basch, Victor. *Schumann.* Translated by Catherine A. Phillips. New York: Alfred A. Knopf, Inc., 1931.

Bedford, Herbert. *Robert Schumann, His Life and Work.* New York: Harper & Brothers, 1925.

Brion, Marcel. *Schumann and the Romantic Age.* Translated by Geoffrey Sainsbury. New York: The Macmillan Company, 1956.

Burk, John N. *Clara Schumann, a Romantic Biography.* New York: Random House, Inc., 1940.

Einstein, Alfred. *Music in the Romantic Era, a History of Musical Thought in the 19th Century.* New York: W. W. Norton & Company, Inc., 1947.

Erskine, John. *Song Without Words: The Story of Felix Mendelssohn.* New York: Julian Messner, Inc., 1941.

Kolodin, Irving (ed.). *The Composer as Listener, a Guide to Music.* New York: Horizon Press, Inc., 1958.

Litzmann, Berthold. *Clara Schumann, An Artist's Life.* Translated by Grace E. Hadow. London: The Macmillan Company, Ltd., 1913.

May, Florence. *The Girlhood of Clara Schumann: Clara Wieck and Her Time.* London: George Bell & Sons, Ltd., 1888.

Niecks, Frederick. *Robert Schumann.* New York: E. P. Dutton & Company, Inc., 1925.

Schauffler, Robert Haven. *Florestan, the Life and Work of Robert Schumann.* New York: Henry Holt & Company, 1945.

———. *Franz Schubert, the Ariel of Music.* New York: G. P. Putnam's Sons, 1949.

Schumann, Robert. *Schumann's Early Letters.* Translated by May Herbert. London: George Bell & Sons, Ltd., 1888.

Wasielewski, Wilhelm Joseph V. *Robert Schumann.* Leipzig: Breitkopf & Hartel, 1906.

Weinstock, Herbert. *Chopin, the Man and His Music.* New York: Alfred A. Knopf, Inc., 1949.